MW00628073

The
Art
Of
Engagement

How to Build
A Strong
Foundation
Of Communication
For Marriage

By David W. & Sheila G. Epstein

Recommended
For Engaged
And Recently Married Couples

Isaac Nathan Publishing Co., Inc.
Los Angeles, California

The Art of Engagement:
How to Build a Strong Foundation of
Communication for Marriage

© Copyright 1983, 1996,

by the Isaac Nathan Publishing Co., Inc.
Los Angeles, California

Revised Edition

Library of Congress Catalog Card Number 96-067068

Library of Congress Cataloging-in-Publication Data
David W. & Sheila G. Epstein
    The Art of Engagement: How to Build a Strong Foundation of
    Communication for Marriage
    1. Pre-Marriage Instruction   2. Wedding Preparation
    3. Marriage Preparation   4. Communication in Marriage

ISBN 0-914615-16-5

Manufactured in the United States of America
Isaac Nathan Publishing Co., Inc.
22711 Cass Avenue, Woodland Hills, CA 91364
(818) 225-9631

Contents

With special thanks to JoAnne Haag, married to "Butch" for 32 years.

Authors' Note

Twenty years ago we found ourselves immersed in the Marriage Encounter Movement. Although we were a Jewish couple, we first experienced a Catholic Marriage Encounter Weekend that changed our lives. We discovered that the original "feelings" of our then eighteen-year marriage were still alive and well, just covered over with the baggage of everyday married life. For a number of years we facilitated Jewish Marriage Encounter weekends, and then, with the help of rabbis and a very special priest, developed the Jewish Engagement weekend. When we wrote this book, we asked Father Gabriel Calvo, the original founder of Marriage Encounter, for his thoughts. His words sum up what this little book is all about:

> Why do an increasing number of today's couples, who had promised each other eternal love and happiness while engaged, find themselves frustrated and unhappy after their wedding? The experts agree that lack of preparation for marriage is the common denominator. Preparation for marriage is a long and hard process. Most couples never even begin.
>
> As an engaged couple you have to be idealistic with well thought out dreams and goals. You also have to be deeply realistic and aware that people have limitations as well as positive qualities. Not only do people have a real capacity to change and improve themselves, but they have the abilities to overcome many of the obstacles of life—*if they have the will to do so.*
>
> A man and a woman travel the road together toward marriage and family life. Each has the qualities and the limitations characteristic of his/her sex. Each comes from a different family, has had a different education and has passed through different experiences that have marked his/her personality and character. As an engaged couple, there is a profound tendency to love each other. There is a mutual attraction, a longing for true friendship and for happiness together. But, at the same time, there are selfish tendencies that can develop into serious obstacles to later growth and love.
>
> This workbook can be a special opportunity for you. Do not miss it! Remember, a generation of new people is watching you, is waiting for you, is challenging you, because that generation is within both of you. All you need is to take the time for—*Reading, Thinking, & Sharing.*

> **Father Gabriel Calvo,** Director, **F.I.R.E.S.**
> Family Intercommunications Relationships and Experiences Services, Inc.
> Washington D.C.
> *Founder of Marriage Encounter*

The
Art
Of
Engagement

How to Build
a Strong Foundation
of Communication
for Marriage

Introduction

This is a workbook. It requires your commitment in order to accomplish its goals. If we, the authors, just wanted to make statements or present a thesis, we would have written a big, thick book.

The Story of This Workbook.

We created this workbook because we think we have something important for couples entering into marriage. In our almost forty years of marriage, and during nine years of working with married and engaged couples, we believe we have learned a great deal. We wish to pass it on to you.

We do not come to you as professionals, with letters after our names, with credentials or degrees. We present to you simply what we have learned, what we have observed, what we have experienced and what we have seen. We come to you as equals, loving marriage, believing in marriage, advocating marriage, and caring for you and your coming marriage.

We care about the future. We believe that the future will be greatly affected by the condition of marriage in the coming years.

About the Material.

We originally believed that the primary basis of this program originated about thirty-five years ago in Spain under the leadership of Father Gabriel Calvo. We were wrong. In times we spent with him, both in our home during his travels and during our own travels, he pointed out to us that the primary basis was our Jewish Scriptures, known to Christians as the Old Testament.

We talked. We searched. We asked. We studied.

For five years during the late 70's and early 80's, we facilitated Jewish Marriage Encounter weekends. We participated in and presented programs with Catholic Marriage Encounter, Episcopal Marriage Encounter, Methodist and Lutheran Marriage Encounters.

We participated in Catholic Engaged Encounter. We developed the Jewish Engaged Experience by combining many of the techniques we observed in the Catholic Engaged Encounter with the ethics and reasoning developed primarily from our membership in the Brandeis-Bardin Institute in California, then under the leadership of Dennis Prager and Rabbi Joseph Telushkin.

Hundreds of couples and dozens of clergy have touched us along the way. Our gift to you, in the form of this workbook, is the result of all their caring for us and for you.

This is a Workbook!

This workbook makes very few statements. It doesn't give any answers either, although many are implied. This workbook poses a lot of questions; questions that must be faced if you are seriously interested in building a strong foundation of communication for your marriage.

To follow this workbook to your best advantage requires a joint commitment. Arrange for time together without distraction. Plan a full weekend, or one hour segments each week over the time necessary to complete the program. You might even decide to share this program with another couple.

Each chapter requires reading, thinking, talking, writing and sharing together. Each chapter follows from the previous chapter. The questions of one chapter are based on the level of communication advanced from the chapter(s) before. The workbook is meant to be a building process and not to be handled with random chapter selection.

Two Bound Journals

Before you begin, purchase two bound journals, approximately notebook size. Select a journal that will be comfortable for you to write extended letters. Pick nice journals because you will probably want to keep them as special keepsakes to be cherished in the years to come.

We hope that you will enjoy this program. We hope that you will choose to follow it as directed so that you can most effectively begin to build a solid foundation of communication for your lives and your marriage.

Pen and Paper Exercises

This workbook requires your active participation if you want to receive the full benefit of the program. We recommend the following procedures:

1. All reading, exercises and discussing must be done together, as a couple . . . not apart or in different places.

2 . Plan to finish only one chapter with each sitting. Don't try to do too much each time. There is enough material in each chapter to keep your minds active for a long time.

3. Do each chapter together, but away from family, friends and other people. The time you spend on this program is *private time together*, not social time with others. Set an atmosphere of specialness. It will be time when you will be working on your relationship, nothing else.

4 . Read the chapters to each other, out loud. Stop and talk about the questions raised. Cover them all. Take your time.

5 . The exercises at the end of each chapter require writing. An additional set of questions is at the back of this book which should be cut out and placed in one of your journals. When you begin the exercises, one of you should keep this workbook, using the questions at the end of the chapter, while the other uses the extra set of questions.

6 . When writing your answers to the exercise questions, separate from each other. Sit across the room or in a different room. All of your attention should be on the paper and what you are writing, not on your finance(e). You will be far more open and honest when you write than if you simply talked. Do not talk while writing.

7. When you are both finished, come back together and exchange your writings. You might read them to each other, or simply exchange them. Either way, make no comments. Read and **listen** carefully to each others' words.

8. When you are both finished reading, put down the writings and start discussing what you have read. Talk about whatever you want, but try to stay on the subject. Try to sense when it is time to finish the formal session. After each session, you have the whole time period before you begin the next chapter to go back over various important points of your discussions.

9. Remember, you are both working for the same thing, a stronger, more open relationship. **Trust one another.**

Special Note.

The writing portion is an important and crucial part of this program. We realize that it is easier, and less threatening to talk together instead of writing, but it is far less effective. When you write, you can place thoughts and ideas directly onto paper without interruption. When you talk, you make adjustments, even as you talk, based on your perceived understanding of how the other person is reacting. Your writing is the most honest you. Do the writing portions as a special gift of love to your fiance(e).

CHAPTER ONE
THE
SEARCH
FOR
MYSELF

Note: For this chapter ONLY, have about ten pages of loose-leaf ruled note paper or a legal pad for some private writing. In the chapters that follow you will be writing in your journals.

Self-acceptance is essential for me to build a relationship with another person. I can't love you until I can at least begin to love myself.

For me to love myself requires that I look deep into myself, and that means that I have to allow myself to be vulnerable, even if only to myself. I have to trust myself enough to honestly look at myself.

Who I Really Am.

My most difficult task is to find the person I really am. I don't really know myself because I usually don't take the time necessary to explore who I am.

Oh yes, I think about myself, and often too. Alone in my car on the freeway or awake in bed in the morning, an hour before the alarm goes off can be sensitive, searching times. But it is so hard to keep my mind from wandering or being diverted to places other than where it belongs.

Pen and Paper Exercises.

I have found that it takes physical effort, an openness, a pen and paper, as well as my mind to carry on a meaningful search. Our minds and our pens and paper are needed to make this program work for us. This workbook constantly talks about action—taking action to accomplish desired results. To get the most out of this workbook will require us to work together and to make the decision to act when asked to write.

I am Seen in Many Different Ways.

We are going to discuss four ways to help us know ourselves better:

1. *The Image I Project to Others.*

2. *How Others See me.*

3. *How I See Myself.*

4. *The Unique Me.*

1. The Image I Project to Others.

The image I project to others is the me that I let others see. It's the kind of person I want others to see. It is how I usually behave when others are around. This image conveys my best qualities, because I want to be liked by others.

For example:

I might project the image of a humorist or a critic. I might project the image of a sophisticated or educated person. I might project the image of the *"with it,"* the *'"Rock,"* Mr. Macho,* or the self-assured person.

I can often hide behind these images to avoid showing other sides of me I don't want others to see.

I might project a happy-go-lucky image to hide my serious side. Another time I might project *Mr. Cool* in order to hide my insecure feelings. I might project a tough, manly image to hide my feelings of tenderness and gentleness.

2. How Others See Me.

I can recognize other peoples' views of me through the positive or negative comments I receive from them. It is through their compliments that they often tell me how they see me.

Because I understand that their comments indicate their view of me, I often find their comments are hard to accept. I don't often see myself as other people do.

13

For example:

> "When I am complimented on my, personal appearance, such as how, I look in a new suit, I get very defensive. I don't see their view of me. I don't get dressed up very often, and I know I tend to ignore my clothing. Even when I am dressed up I believe that I should have taken the time to really fix up the finer points of my appearance.

> "In the same vein, if I am complimented on my friendliness I usually grin and change the subject. I see myself as generally shy in strange situations and perhaps a little stand-offish. I don't see myself as outgoing and friendly.

> "When complimented on something I've done, I tend to belittle whatever the accomplishment is. I usually point out that it was based on common sense, timing or good luck, and that almost an anyone else could or would have done the same thing under the same circumstances. I see myself as not doing enough. I generally find it difficult to accept a compliment about something I believe I should have done even better."

3. How I See Myself.

At times, my self-image isn't very good. It can be when I'm alone, driving home at night, or when I'm surrounded by people, in a crowded room or at a party. There are certain times I tend to think the worst of myself, to dwell on my weak points instead of the strong ones.

At times such as these I tend to compare myself with others and see them as better than myself. I use a *double standard.*

The Double Standard Most of Us Use.

What is an occasional flaw in others, I tend to accept just as it is, an occasional flaw. What is an occasional flaw in myself I take as a personal branding.

In the same light, what I accept in others as a good trait they need only show as a general rule. For me to accept the same good trait as a part of myself, I demand that I must be perfect to that trait 100% of the time.

For Example:

> *"I have some thoughtful friends. They seem to care a great deal about others. They call. They drop notes, especially for special occasions. Sometimes they miss, but I accept them as thoughtful people.*
>
> *"I care a lot about people and spend a fair amount of time in contact with them. I call. Sometimes I drop notes, especially for special occasions. Sometimes I miss. I judge myself as a less than thoughtful person."*

I use a double standard!

4. The Unique Me.

The real me is not just the image I project, nor how others see me, nor how I see myself. The real me is a unique individual. There is no-one exactly like me anywhere in the world, nor has there every been anyone exactly like me. *I am unique!*

When I look at myself I have to understand that what I may regard as a weakness, others may regard as a sign of strength.

For example:

Gentleness in a man traditionally has not been looked at as manly, yet today, many women look for and want this trait in their mate.

Assertiveness in a woman is rarely considered a feminine quality, but is often desired and looked for by many men today.

Honesty in the business world is far too often looked down upon as outmoded, yet many people prefer a slower, but more honest route to success by their mate than a faster, questionable, but socially acceptable way.

Patience in our fast society is often looked at as slowness or indecision. But some prefer a more careful, thought-out type individual as their partner.

As Humans, We Are Different!

There are no good or evil animals or plants. Non-human entities live by genes and by environment. Their choices are decided by instinct or chemical reaction or circumstances. Animals move by hunger, reproductive and survival instincts. Plants grow and move by chemical and physical circumstances. Their goal is life and the perpetuation of their species.

This workbook is predicated on the concept that, as human beings, we are above the level of plants and animals. We are created in the image of God and not, as claimed by some currently popular notions, *"at one with nature."*

As a human, I am unlike any other known creature in our universe. I am unique. As a human being, I have the ability to choose *to be* good or not *to be* good, to choose *to do* good or not *to do* good, *to decide to love* or *not to love*. I have the ability *to choose* to do more than just be alive!

I have been given the ability to make my own choices in life and I am solely responsible for all the choices I make. My marriage and my life are either positively or negatively affected by those choices. You, likewise, are affected by the choices you make.

The real me is a unique person, one of a kind, a unique set of genes and circumstances, created by God, and possessed of a "Divine spark," the ability to choose between good and evil, to choose between right and wrong, to decide to love or not to love.

The choice you and your future life partner have made together to work through this book can result in a fuller and more rewarding marriage and future. The benefits you receive will depend entirely on your decision to do the work that is required to complete the exercises.

This workbook is about one particular type of decision, one kind of choice we can learn to make alone or together that can result in a full and rewarding marriage.

A Pen and Paper Exercise.

What follows is a set of questions. Choose who will use the workbook. The other will use the Chapter One question in the pages previously cut from the back of this book.

Next separate from each other, where you can write without distracting each other, preferably in separate rooms, or at least across the room.

Plan on a minimum of twenty and a maximum of about thirty minutes for this first exercise. This time, and this time only, when you are finished writing you will not share your answers with each other. Instead, put them away in some other private place.

Answer each question completely. It may be helpful to outline each answer first with words or a short phrases. Then go back and write out your answers more fully.

Remember, you are writing only to yourself this time. You will not be sharing your answers for this chapter.

I always know how honest I am when I am writing. I know that to be effective I have to dig deep, trust myself and use my pen and paper to its fullest.

The final questions at the end of each chapter are to be done in writing rather than thinking or talking about them. If we try to "think it out" we find our minds adjusting ideas, hiding ideas, and avoiding our search, especially if we are sharing with our fiance(e). The pen and paper can be magic in our search for ourselves and as a basis for the beginning of meaningful communication together.)

Questions - Chapter One - The Search for Myself.

1. What are some of the specific good qualities I would like others to see in me? What are some of the nice things about me that I would like other people to notice?

2. What qualities do others see in me? *(Give a few examples of comments you tend to receive from others.)*

3. How do I see myself? *(What is my self-image?)*

   What do I like about myself? *(Be specific.)*

   What do I dislike about myself? *(Explain in detail)*

4. What specific personal characteristics do I see in myself that I think make it more difficult for you (my fiancee) to love me?

5. What changes do I think I need to make in myself to become more loving and lovable to you?

Remember, this writing is private and for your eyes only. When the time is up, put these pages away and go on to the next chapter together.

CHAPTER TWO

LOVE
IS A
DECISION

THE RECURRING STAGES OF LOVE

Three Recurring Stages.

There are three recurring stages of love. These stages are true to most relationships, literally all marriages, and often to times of engagement. The knowledge and understanding of these stages can better prepare us for their occurrence and give us direction and insight for handling them as they do occur in our lives.

The "Illusion" Period, Better Known as *Romance.*

Romance is that special time when we are first attracted to one another. There is an awareness of a special bond, a taut rubberband, drawing two people together. It is a special period, full of anticipation, fast flowing adrenaline, the stuff from which romantic movies are made.

Romance can be a time of silliness, a time of excitement, of distracted emotions. The whole world shines. The flowers are more colorful. The skies are their bluest. There are not enough words in any language to paint the pictures we draw with our minds and hearts when we first discover our love for each other.

Romance is a time of illusion. We have met the *"perfect person."* All our focus is on love. We see each other's good points so well.

> *"She lets me make the decisions."*
>
> *"She is so easy going."*
>
> *"She is frugal, doesn't make me spend my money."*
>
> *"He is so punctual."*
>
> *"He is so organized."*
>
> *"He is so ambitious."*

Simple things bring us joy—a touch, a kiss, a simple walk, a short ride, a soda, a greeting card, talking together forever about everything and anything.

Our romance gives us the habit of thinking of the *other* person. We focus on what pleases the *other* person and doing things for him/her.

Our romance is God's gift to get us out of being *self*-centered and becoming *other*-centered.

The Period Called "Disillusionment."

The second stage of love is "Disillusionment." It can be a time of reality awareness when we are able to see more clearly the entire person or our entire marriage or our entire relationship.

During the "Romance Period" many little things that could have caused irritation, may have been overlooked.

Disillusionment is the time when those negative character traits we might possess, or those not-so perfect parts of our relationship become as equally visible as our romance.

To make matters worse is the fact that we originally refused to acknowledge those negative or bothersome traits. Now we see them clearly and that makes them stand out even more. All of a sudden, instead of focusing on my *partner* and our relationship, I find myself focusing back more on *myself* and my frustrations in having to deal with the now evident negative aspects of my partner.

"She lets me make the decisions."

> *"Before we married I bad made most of the decisions. It seemed easier that way. She deferred them to me and was so accepting. But I never expected I'd have to make all the decisions in our day to day life. I didn't want to be the decorator, pick out our household furnishings, decide where and when we'd go out for entertainment. That was her job. I was starting a career. I had more important, worldly things to do. I found myself frustrated with having to make all the little household decisions. She seemed unable to make decisions at all. The fun times, the people, the places, the things we were going to do together only seemed to get started if I initiated them."*

"She is so easy going."

> *"My young bride was so easy going even to the point that our apartment wasn't important to her. The dust balls in the corners and the dark ring on the walls, about thirty inches above the floor (from our daughter's dirty hands) are my major recollection of our earliest home. Only "Fibber McGee" could have had more stuffed closets than ours. I can recall the number of times that I got angry because I didn't have an ironed shirt and the laundry basket was overflowing on our bedroom floor."*

21

THE ART OF ENGAGEMENT

"She is so frugal, doesn't make me spend my money."

"She wasn't just frugal and concerned about money. She was tight! She couldn't spend money. It wasn't that she kept me from spending or even wasting money, she just wouldn't spend any on herself. I would have to push her to buy clothes for herself or to spend anything."

"He is so punctual."

"After we were married it seemed he always insisted we be on time, even a little early. Whenever we went out, he would yell at me to make sure I was ready five or ten minutes early. I can't remember how many, times we arrived at a home to be met by a hostess in her bathrobe or by her husband who was still getting dressed.

"If he had a special appointment he would wake me up to make breakfast so he could leave thirty minutes early. When he had a flight, I would have to take him to the airport hours before the plane was due to leave. He was always worried that something might go wrong and he'd miss his plane. His punctuality haunted me."

"He is so organized."

"Nothing ever went wrong with anything he planned. Nothing went wrong because he planned for every eventuality, literally everything including earthquakes, tornados and tidal waves, just in case. Any medium or large size event would become a nightmare for me. He expected everything planned out his way, weeks in advance and down to the last detail (And everything had to be on time, too.) He made the decisions, he made the plans, and I'd better do them his way, and at the exact time he specified for every item."

"He is so ambitious."

"He was so ambitious. He worked hard and long hours. He sought out promotions and advantageous job changes. We moved from city to city, from New England to the South, to the Midwest, to the Southwest, to the West Coast, picking up possessions and children along the way. I seemed to spend all my time cooking, baby caring, packing or unpacking in strange places.

"His life seemed exciting. He sure was ambitious. He was working with exciting people, spending weeks on the road away from home. He was getting to see the country while I saw only the same apartment with only different-named supermarkets down the block. I was proud of his ambition, but he was around very little to share his life with me.

"During the times he was home, he always brought loads of paperwork with him, reports to be done, or ideas he was proposing. His ambition took away from our time, even when we were home together."

As many of the traits we originally admired in each other seem to turn back on us, we often found ourselves refocusing away from each other and becoming more self-centered again.

As I become more self-centered, I experience the loneliness that comes from this disillusionment. In my disillusionment I take my eyes off my partner and our relationship and instead, focus on myself and the things that are either being done to me or not being done for me.

I become *"I-centered"* again instead of *"we-centered."* I dwell on myself, my self-pity, even act like a "martyr." I lose sight of the gift we have of one-another.

Many relationships, be they friendships, businesses, romances, or even marriages, cease to exist, or at least to be "alive" at this point. They might appear to live on, but they are over unless both parties do something constructive.

The Stage of "Decision."

Love is a Decision

Love is a decision to behave toward another in a specific manner. This is the only stage that isn't automatic!

Love is a Decision **is the most important concept of the entire program. If this is all that is learned, if this is all that is understood, then all our work will have been worth the effort. We will be on the way to building a solid foundation for a lifetime of marriage.**

In the not too distant past, someone expressed the idea that love is a *feeling,* and sadly, the idea caught on. From this concept, from this emotional idea, grew a great sorrow of our modern times.

As love became accepted simply as a *feeling,* the cement that held marriages together started to crumble. Emotional *feeling* became more important than *deeds or actions. Feelings* superseded all the lessons of the past. <u>Feelings</u> superseded relationships, family, even children. This *supreme focus on feelings* has bequeathed to us a society filled with loneliness, sorrow, emptiness and hurt.

This is not to say that we should judge feelings as right or wrong, not advocate that we ignore them, follow them, cover them up or expose them. What we are saying is that *feelings are not the ultimate value* on which we base our decisions.

Love is a decision, not a feeling. Love is how I decide to behave toward you. Love is action. Love is doing. Love is being *other*-centered instead of *self*-centered just as it is in our periods of romance.

Love is *acting* loving, even when I don't *feel* loving.

The action of loving shapes my heart far more than the heart shapes my actions. When I don't feel loving, I can take action by *acting* loving. More often then not, I then "feel" loving as a result of my behavior.

Love is a decision to love you even when you are *not lovable* in my eyes.

Love is a decision when I allow myself *to be loved* by you even when I don't see myself as lovable. (This is really hard.)

Understanding that *love is a decision* can lead me, can lead us, away from terrible times of loneliness and/or disillusionment.

But love takes action. I have to act loving by *doing* loving things or I must accept love by *accepting* loving things. I must make a *decision to love* or a *decision to be loved.*

The third stage of the recurring cycle of love is making a *decision to love.* This is when we both put aside our renewed self-centeredness and re-focus back on to each other. We focus on our joy of loving each other and of being loved by each other.

Good feelings are nice, but.....

Love is a Decision!

Pen & Paper Exercise.

First write a fast outline or short phrases. Then, rewrite each of them as a letter to your fiance(e). Make each a long letter. Be honest and be open. Understand that your fiance(e) knows you far better than you might believe.

Do not write what you think he/she might want to read. Write the truth. Allow yourself to be vulnerable. It's OK. Remember, *love is a decision.*

When you are both through writing, exchange your letters with each other. Read them quietly. Perhaps you might wish to read them aloud to each other. When you are finished, talk about them. When you believe you have said all there is to say to each other, go on to the next chapter.

Plan about thirty minutes to write your answers to these questions.

Questions - Chapter Two - *Love is a Decision*

1. When do I think I have experienced romance in our relationship?

2. When do I think I have experienced disillusionment in our relationship?

3. When have I made a conscious decision to love you even though I didn't "feel" loving at that time?

4. When have I made a conscious decision to allow you to love me even though I didn't *"feel"* lovable at that time?

5. In what areas of our life do I find that loving you takes a decision? *(Explain fully.)*

6. List two ways you and your fiancee are alike and describe each of them.

7. List two ways you believe you and your fiance(e) differ and describe each of them.

CHAPTER THREE
OPENNESS
IS ALSO
A DECISION

*Openness is the key to communication
in our relationship.*

*Openness is the key to communication
during our engagement.*

*Openness is the key to communication
in our marriage.*

Openness has a dual definition.

A.   *My revealing the real me to you.*

This definition of *openness* means having trust in myself to reveal my inner *feelings* to you, and not just my opinions, thoughts and ideas. I have to be able to share what is going on inside of me with you, my fears, my hopes, my physical and mental *feelings*.

B.   *My listening to you reveal yourself to me.*

This second part of the definition of openness is being able to listen to you share yourself with me. I have to train myself to block out of my mind, as best I can, my *reactions* to hearing what you say at the moment you are saying it, and put all my efforts into trying to fully *understand* what you are trying to communicate to me BEFORE I respond or react.

"When I only listen to his words, all I really can get from hearing him are words and ideas, plain and flat. By the use of non-verbal techniques I am better able to experience the person behind the words.

"I try to listen, not only to his words, but to the tone of his voice. Does he sound like the words that he is using or is he really saying something else? I listen for a quiet voice, whether it is calm and easy or muffled and almost hidden. If his voice is loud, I listen to hear whether it is fast and shrill or firm and solid. I also listen for the sounds of silence. Tone, pitch, loudness and speed, each of these qualities of sound often tell me more than his spoken words. It is all a matter of listening.

"I also try to watch him carefully, for movement while I am listening. Is he calm or nervous, fidgety or relaxed, tense or cozy? A clenching fist or a tapping foot can tell me so much more. How fast is he breathing? Is he sitting tall or slouched over?

"I watch his eyes. They are said to be the windows of our souls. Eyes can tell as much as words. Can he look at me with solid eye contact or do his eyes dart from one object to another? Are they soft and warm or hard and cold?

"If I hold his hand, is it warm or cold, relaxed or tense. If I am sitting by him is his body at ease or is it stiff. Is he still or is he moving about?"

The sounds we hear and the body we see all communicate as much to us as words we listen to. To listen completely to you requires my fullest attention. This type of listening takes a lot of constant practice.

Vulnerability.

A major effect of openness is vulnerability. To allow myself to be open with you I have to allow myself to be vulnerable. I have to make a conscious decision to take that chance. That is why we say that *openness is a decision.*

Openness reveals to you my inner self, my feelings, my vulnerability. Not only does it show my faults, but it leaves me with the potential of being misunderstood and unaccepted by you. On the other hand, openness also demonstrates my need for your love.

Openness requires that I believe in myself, that I trust myself to be open with you. I have to believe that I am basically a good person and that other people love me as I am.

Openness means believing in my goodness and believing in your goodness.

Openness is trusting that you love me and accept me as I am.

Openness is based on trust that develops from the sharings between us through our engagement period and then on through our marriage. Each day of our lives there will be something new for us to share on which we can further build our trust.

Openness starts innocently with our time of romance. Our engagement is a special time for the conscious development of our openness to one another.

Openness is essential for a marriage that is to grow and be fulfilling.

Now, during our engagement, is the time for us to build a solid foundation of openness for our marriage.

29

Risk.

Openness means making a decision to trust you.

Openness means making a decision to trust myself.

> *"I usually have a reluctance to share my dreams, beliefs, values, and goals in life with other people. I don't usually share my feelings, my relationships with my parents, my attitudes about sex and my attitudes about money with others.*
>
> *"I have fears of looking foolish, of being rejected, of being wrong or possibly even risking losing you."*

Openness is Worth the Risk!

If we don't build openness in our relationship, little by little, bit by bit, we will find ourselves sowing seeds for later disillusionment in our marriage.

Now, during our engagement, is the time for us to build foundations of trust rather than walls of protection. A strong marriage is built on foundations of trust.

A weak marriage dissolves when surrounded by walls of separation. These walls are created by our failure to take the risks necessary to build a relationship based on openness.

Openness is Not . . .

Openness is not frankness.

When I am frank, I am not concerned only how my words will affect you. I'm only interested with my statement.

Openness is not *"Peace at Any Price."*

Many people have a *"Live and Let Live—Don't Rock the Boat"* marriage. By living this way, they are more like roommates than a couple. They settle for much less than full potential for their marriage.

Openness is not confessing past deeds or actions.

Openness means sharing myself—me, not my deeds. Openness is *person* oriented, not *action or deed* oriented.

Openness Can be the Willingness to Argue.

Arguing can be healthy, but only if it is constructive arguing. Constructive arguing can build a better relationship. Constructive arguing can build foundations for better communication.

Destructive arguing can destroy a relationship. Failing to argue can build walls that impede communication.

A constructive argument can make a relationship grow and be healthy . . .

. . . but there are rules to follow.

31

Some Rules for Arguing

1. Avoid name calling—except *"Honey," "Dear," "Sweetheart,"* and not said sarcastically. Remember with whom you are arguing.

2. Avoid third parties. It is just between us. Don't bring in parents, friends, or in-laws for your side of the argument.

3. Avoid past histories. Anything more than two or three days old is a past history.

4. Stick to the subject. Other topics are for other times.

5. Don't throw your partner's weaknesses up in his/her face. You might win the argument, but you could destroy your relationship.

6. Don't part angrily. Ask yourself constantly, *"How important is this argument subject in terms of our total relationship?"*

7. Maintain a sense of humor.

8. Hold hands while arguing. This is the hardest rule to follow, because it takes a ***decision to love.*** It is guaranteed to keep your focus where it belongs, ***on each other.***

Pen and Paper Exercises.

As in the last chapter, write your answers while apart. Come together afterwards to share and discuss what you have written.

Estimated writing time is thirty minutes.

Questions - Chapter Three - *Openness is Also a Decision*

1. What positive things about myself (thoughts, feelings, hopes, dreams) do I find difficult to reveal to you?

2. What negative things about myself, do I find difficult to reveal to you?

3. In what areas of our relationship have I been afraid to risk being open with you? (Explain)

4. In what areas of our relationship do I think you have been afraid to risk being open with me? (Explain).

   Draw your answers from the areas listed below for each of the questions above.

   a. Our responsibilities in our marriage.

   b. Our roles in our marriage.

   c. Our sex life.

   d. Our children.

   e. Our religion.

   f. Our in-laws.

g.   Our money.

h.   Our drinking or drug habits.

i.   Our careers - yours and mine.

j.   The way you treat me.

k.   Our friends - yours and mine.

l.   Our health - yours and mine.

m.   Other areas. (Explain).

5. Do I think I listen to you?

6. Do I think you listen to me?

CHAPTER FOUR

SIGNPOSTS OF A CLOSED RELATIONSHIP

The purpose of this chapter is to demonstrate that marriage is not just living together as friends or as roommates.

Marriage can be a growing relationship that calls us, each day of our lives, to a lifelong commitment to strive to become totally involved with one another.

This is not the message of today's media, where love, marriage and other relationships are based on "now" feelings and what feels good.

This workbook is based on the concept that lifelong love is a *decision*, an action, and not a feeling. Love takes action, constant action, even when we don't "feel" loving or "feel" lovable.

The reward of the *decision to love*—and the action of loving or allowing ourselves to be loved—is a growing and solid marriage.

What Makes a Closed Relationship?

We build our personal walls in circles.

Each of us forms expectations or attitudes, about ourselves, each other, our lives and our marriage. This is an on-going process throughout our lives. However, if we don't share these attitudes, or these expectations with each other, and share them on a day to day basis, we soon find ourselves closed to each other. Each of us finds ourselves behind our own private circle of walls.

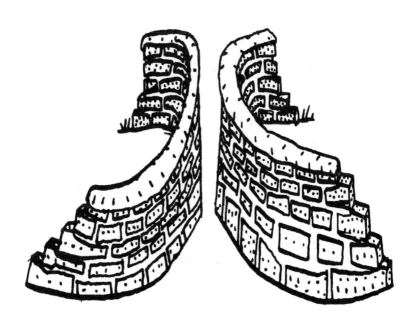

We build our personal circle of walls in a sequence — somewhat like this . . . .

1. I develop some new attitude about, say, our marriage.

2. I don't share this attitude with you. I simply don't tell you about it.

3. You then don't live up to my new, unshared expectations.

4. So, I get upset with you.

5. I turn inward, away from focusing on you and thinking more of myself.

6. You don't know why I'm upset because I never shared my new expectations with you.

7. You get upset with me for my outward negative reactions to you.

8. You get protective of yourself, taking your focus off of me and on to yourself.

9. We both become walled off from each other, at least in this area.

10. We focus more and more on ourselves instead of each other in our daily lives.

11. We consciously or unconsciously look for other areas to build even more walls to keep us apart.

12. Circles of walls beget more circles of walls.

Growing and Changing.

It is making *decisions to love* that help us be open and trusting with each other. We grow as individuals as we are loved by each other. The more we are loved, the more we become free to be ourselves. I must trust you, as my fiancee, to be open with me. I must trust myself, as your fiancee, to be open with you.

As husband and wife, we will be the greatest single influence on each other. We will be a greater influence than our parents, friends, teachers or even bosses and working associates. As we love each other, we will grow and we will change. Our loving each other is the support that each of us needs to be able to grow and develop our fullest capacity as human beings.

I can love you, but I cannot, nor should not, expect to change you.

You might change because I have changed. But I can't expect to change you. Only you can change yourself. Neither should you expect to change me. Only I can change myself.

My loving you, or lack of loving you, can build your self-image, or lower it, and that can bring about change or growth. But you change yourself. You make the decision and take the steps necessary to change yourself.

The love and openness I receive from you may make me freer—freer to change, freer to grow. But I change myself. I make the decision to change and take the steps necessary to change myself.

We can only help create an atmosphere for each other to grow and to change. We can't change each other. It never works!

What does work is our actively loving each other so fully, so completely, that we develop inner confidence and strength to grow and change on our own.

We have to ask ourselves and ask each other two serious questions <u>now</u>, while we are engaged.

1. *Can I live with you without expecting any changes on your behalf?*

2. *Do I think you can you live with me without expecting any changes on my behalf?*

Our Expectations before Marriage.

We usually have a lot of pre-conceived ideas about what marriage is or is not.

There is a tendency to avoid our differences before marriage for a number of reasons.

1. *I simply don't want to rock the boat.*

2. *Rejection is hard for me to take.*

3. *I have a fear of losing you.*

As we read this chapter together we have to try and put these fears aside. We have to try and trust in our love for each other. We have to try to understand that our love is stronger than our fears.

We often expect marriage to be what we are currently used to as singles, with a lot of personal freedom, and responsibility basically only to ourselves.

There are a lot of areas we have to talk about. These are everyday examples that may have to be adjusted when we are living together after our wedding.

We should question some simple areas of our lifestyle that might have to be adjusted after we are married.

Do I like to sleep late?
Do you like to get up early?

Do I like vacations away?
Do you like to stay at home?

Do I like a neatly decorated home?
Do you seem not to care?

Do I procrastinate?
Are you always on schedule?

Is fashion important to me?
Is clothing unimportant to you?

Do I have to plan everything?
Are you impulsive?

Am I a spender?
Are you a saver?

Do I like sports?
Do you hate sports?

Do I watch a lot of TV?
Do you avoid TV?

Do I like the window open at night?
Do you like the window closed?

Do I like a lot of guests?
Do you prefer privacy?

These are not the "big deals" in life, but they are important for us to be aware of, to discuss, and to understand before our marriage. How many other simple areas of our life-styles can you think of that might need to be adjusted after we are married?

We tend to recognize these differences before we are married, but we also tend to ignore the fact that these differences might affect our marriage.

We often think that we can change the other person,
but we can't!

There are more serious differences we might have to face before our marriage. They can't wait to be discussed until later.

These differences might include:

Drinking or Drugs.

> Will you/I quit after we're married?

> Am I expected to follow along with your habits?

Relationships with Family.

> Will you (finally) get to like my family after we're married?

> Will they (finally) get to like you?

> Will I (finally) get to like your family after we're married?

> Will they (finally) get to like me?

> How will all this affect our marriage?

Relationships with Old Single Friends.

> Will you stop having <u>frequent</u> nights out with your single friends after our marriage?

> Will I stop having <u>frequent</u> nights out with my single friends after our marriage?

What other serious areas do you believe should be open for discussion now?

These are differences that we have to discuss before our marriage. They will not automatically go away after our wedding ceremony.

Our problems may or may not be solved, but at least they will be understood as problems and areas of differences for us to work on before and after our marriage.

Talked about now, brought honestly into the open, they can be shared and worked on together so that they won't come as surprises later on.

Love and marriage
don't make differences go away!

Religion.

Our religion(s) is a specific area that needs discussion. It is something that, one way or another, will be with each of us all our lives.

We have to ask about and discuss our differences now.

If we have the same faith we have to ask each other:

How do our attitudes differ about our faith?

How might our different family backgrounds affect our lives?

How might our different families' expectations affect our lives?

Is one of us observant and one not? How might this affect our marriage?

How will we handle our religious practices?

What part, if any, will our religion play in our day-to-day lives?

How will we handle the religious education of our children?

If we are of different faiths we have to investigate all the questions before and then also discuss the potential tensions between our family backgrounds as well as our families. Extra questions are:

What are my religious expectations?

What do I think are your religious expectations?

What do I think are our religious expectations?

How will we handle different holidays?

Where will we celebrate different religious holidays?

How do we bring up the children?

To bring up children without any religious background, allowing them to "choose" for themselves when older is depriving them of an important childhood experience. It can only cause them confusion instead of building meaningful values.

What about conversion?

If one of us is planning to convert, it is important that we both fully understand the reason why.

Is this to be a conversion of faith, a solid series of bricks and mortar in our marriage foundation?

or . . .

Is this to be a conversion of convenience, one that could turn out later to be just sand in the cement?

We have to remember that even with conversion, our childhood background and upbringing remains the same. We have to be fully aware that tensions may arise from these differences.

Family Backgrounds.

We would all like to believe that our differences will not cause us any problems, they'll just go away after marriage. But, love and marriage won't make our differences go away. And if they are not dealt with before marriage, they can be become a source of future difficulties in our marriage.

Marriage requires a lot of decision making, constant communication and hard work to remain an open relationship. Our individual family backgrounds will greatly effect our marriage relationship. We must to look those differences now and discuss them—*before* our wedding.

Where might our experienced different family backgrounds affect our marriage?

Do I come from a warm family?
> *Do you come from a reserved family?*

Is my family demonstrative?
> *Is your family stand-offish?*

Does my family tend to encourage individual pursuits?
> *Does your family prefer family togetherness?*

Do I really accept your family?
> *Do I think you really accept my family?*

What other family background areas are of concern to you? Talk about them now.

The *Perceived* Problem Often Isn't the *Real* Problem.

Our perceived problem may not necessarily be our real problem. Our real problem is that we tend to believe our differences will not cause any problems in our marriage.

We must acknowledge our differences now and either accept them as they are, or we agree to work on them now to avoid being surprised by them later on. Perhaps they will always be with us and that's OK.

More Questions to be Shared.

Are my attitudes the same or different from yours regarding . . .

Careers and Ambitions.

Is my success more important to me than our marriage?

Do I think success is more important to you than our marriage?

Whose career is to come first if we each have one?

If my career requires moving to new locations, how will it effect your career?

If your career requires moving to new locations, how will it effect my career?

Does career come before family life?

Children

Will we have children?
When will we have a family?

Will we postpone our family because of my career?

Will we postpone our family because of your career?

Will we postpone our family because its convenient?

Do I believe children are a blessing or do I believe they are a problem and that they will tie us down?

Do I want the responsibility of a family?

Do I think you want the responsibility of a family?

Can we handle the responsibility children will bring?

If we disagree about having children do I expect to give in?

If we disagree about having children do I expect you to give in?

Money and Finances.

Will all money be considered ours no matter who earns it or will we each have control of our own money?

Who will decide our budget?

Who will make the decisions to spend and/or invest our money?

Who will be in charge of balancing the checkbook?

It is easy to overlook or to minimize the fact the some of the topics covered in this chapter might ever come between us. But we would be fooling ourselves if we refused to look at those differences now.

The best time for us to talk about our differences is NOW! —BEFORE our marriage.

Pen and Paper Exercise

Write your answers to all of the questions. *Write the longest answers to the questions you don't want to answer at all!* Be completely honest and trusting.

When you are finished writing, exchange your answers with your fiancee again and read each others' pages. Plan plenty of time to discuss your answers.

Questions - Chapter Four -
Signposts of a Closed Relationship

1. What are the things I talk to others about more easily than I do with you?

    Do I trust someone else more than you? *(at least in some areas). Explain.*

2. Do I think you confide in someone else more than me? Whom do I think it is and why do I think you do?

3. What difficulties do I have with *myself* that hold me back from writing and sharing myself honestly with you now?

    What difficulties do I have with *you* that hold me back from writing and sharing myself honestly with you now?

4. Do I have any doubts about marrying you? What are they?

5. Do I think you have any doubts about marrying me? What might they be?

6. Are our wedding plans primarily shared between us, divided up, or all one-sided?

    Do I think it ought to be shared differently?

7. What are the things that make me angry with you? Explain each item more fully.

8. Am I jealous of you? In what ways?

9. In what areas must I have my own way? Why?

10. What areas am I still afraid to discuss with you? Why?

    What areas do I think you are still afraid to discuss with me? Why?

CHAPTER FIVE

MARRIAGE AS A LIFELONG COMMITMENT

A rich, fulfilling marriage is a lifelong commitment, a lifelong career. It is a covenant with God for us to actively love each other totally and irrevocably. Marriage is for deep, long lasting love, not simply a short period of romance. Marriage is a PUBLIC COMMITMENT, sanctified by and with God through our wedding vows, to live our lives as a couple.

Marriage, as a social institution is a foundation block of Western Civilization. Marriage roots go back to the dawn of human history. Marriage has survived social assaults, legal assaults, philosophical assaults, social derision, fads and much more. In spite of attack after attack, marriage has ultimately survived as the best and most normative way for man and woman to live together.

Marriage is more than a lifelong legal contract. It is not a limited relationship. Marriage is also not the simple stereotyped relationship that television, magazines and the rest of the media constantly spew forth at us.

Marriage can be a unique and active loving relationship between two partners who become more complete individuals through each other and because of each other. *Love is a Decision.* By making this a constant part of our marriage, we can translate the words above into a beautiful, daily reality.

Countless words have been written trying to describe the unique feelings of human romantic love. But words can never truly describe those exciting internal feelings we can experience.

"When Sheila and I courted, I remember being so full of romance. I still remember the sharp feelings of anticipation whenever we were going to be together. I would sit on the edge of my seat while driving to be with her. My heart would be light I would feel it beating. My solar plexus would be tense, excited. I would feel alive and aware.

"When we were together, my whole being centered on Sheila. I listened intently to every word she spoke. I heard and I saw how she presented each idea, each statement, each question. I heard her words. I saw her movements. I watched her face intently listening carefully to her voice. When we were together I would be focused totally on her.

"Whenever we parted, to go home, or back to school, I would feel the loss of her presence. I would remain focused on her words, a remaining scent, or a memory. Music from my car radio sounded of her. Music at home sounded of her. My existence away from Sheila had her in focus, not me. I would fill my emptiness with my awareness of her."

Romantic Feelings.

Initial romantic feelings cannot sustain a lifelong marriage commitment. On the other hand, these same types of feelings can remain as a part of our marriage. Marriage need not settle into forgotten memories as it is constantly depicted in the media of our current culture.

Our media focuses on relationships where these special feelings of romance have gone, been covered up, or simply have ceased to exist. Stories of alive marriages rarely make good reading, good press, good television time or good money. The result is that all we usually have to compare ourselves and our marriage with is what the media projects to us. When we compare our marriage with problem or troubled relationships of TV and movie "media" couples, our marriage tends to look pretty good. So we often settle for what we have instead of reaching for the **best** it could be.

Our love and our marriage can affect other marriages. Our marriage can be a symbol of our heritage, our faith and all that is positive about marriage. Other people who see us have something positive to strive for in their own marriage. Ours can be a positive alternative to the popular culture's negative view of marriage.

Based on an active loving commitment, where the romantic feelings remain alive and well, although perhaps in slightly different forms, can be an inspiration to others and give them hope for their own marriage.

We can actively decide to love one another, every day, no matter how we "feel," and reflect a true commitment by our behavior toward each other. This kind of relationship keeps our focus on one another, and not on ourselves. Making the necessary *decisions to love* is what this workbook is about. Warm romantic feelings are the result of putting its ideas into practice.

Romantic Love.

Romantic love is a special human experience, too intense to maintain. Its purpose is to place us in a situation, a marriage situation, where we can grow more fully as individuals and as a couple. Romantic feelings are the reward of our efforts.

51

"I currently live with a feeling of completeness in most areas of my life. My life has a quiet aura of contentment and fulfillment. It is centered on my wife. I still have feelings of excitement and anticipation when I am about to see her after a working day. It is not the same all-encompassing feeling that it was when we were courting. All the physical characteristics are still there, but the feelings are muted, rounded off at the edges. They roll easily.

"When we are together I feel complete, yet in a more mellow way. When we are apart I have an emptiness that can only be filled by her presence, a quiet yet constant awareness. After thirty-nine years of marriage I remain mostly focused on my mate, and not on myself.

"I have heard it said that the feelings in a good marriage are like a long simmering stew pot on the stove. Originally it consisted of few ingredients, but they were hot and spicy. As time passes, more ingredients (life experiences) are added to the pot, thickening the broth (relationship). As the stew matures it becomes thicker and thicker, tastier and more filling. The original spices may still be there, but they are part of a much more complete taste experience. So it can be with original romantic love as a marriage relationship grows."

Accepting your love affects my self-image.

"There was another aspect to my romantic feelings before we were married, a little harder to admit. When I was with Sheila, I really preferred to be alone with her. I wanted all my attention focused on her and wanted as much of her attention focused on me as possible. But there were times we had to be with others.

"When we were with others I had all the previous feelings, plus a feeling of personal pride. I was a 'big man.' I had this special girlfriend and I believed that made me a better person in the eyes of my friends. 'Look, see what I have.' I believed I stood a little taller and a lot straighter. I believed the image I projected was a better image. Sheila, by her presence, made me think more highly of myself and made me a much more complete person."

We can consciously nurture this area of self-esteem in our marriage. Unlike romantic love, which has to *"round off its edges,"* we can develop this area more fully. The freedom that comes from my better self-image, derived in part through you, can allow me to grow in other areas. I need not be tied simply to the level of plain acceptance by others. You can be the visible affirmation of my goodness.

"Mature marriage isn't an automatic state or feelings. It took many years of inner loneliness, focusing on myself and my self-image before I learned how, to refocus on to Sheila. Only when I started making conscious decisions to love Sheila did my life began to fulfill itself."

How well do I focus on you today?

How well do you focus on me today?

Making a Conscious Decision to Love You— an Important Part of My Life.

When I listen to you share your thoughts, your feelings or your day with me, do I listen completely?

Do I try to "hear" you or am I reacting to what you're saying?

Do I start planning my response while you're still talking?

Do I give you my full attention instead of sharing you with my newspaper or television at the same time?

Do I show an interest in each aspect of your strengths?

Do I encourage your endeavors, your search for achievement, education or whatever your special interests are?

Do I help you with your weak spots by using some of my complementary strengths where you might otherwise stumble or shy away?

Do I support and help you, even when it is in an area that does not hold much interest for me, especially when you need my help?

Do I often take our relationship for granted?

How do I think you would respond to the questions above? Pick one or two specifically.

How do I think you should respond to the questions above? Pick one or two specifically.

Marriage is a 100%-100% Proposition!

Marriage allows us to love one another completely without keeping score, without my giving half and waiting for you to match it.

Our current culture talks about marriage as a 50/50 proposition; *"You give to me and I will give equally to you."* It sounds right, but because we are human, it has a built-in destructive feature.

If one of us fails the other, in any way or in any degree, we risk the slowing down of our mutual support. 50% becomes 47%, 47% becomes 40%, 40% becomes 30%, and so on until we find ourselves separate people, giving very little to each other. We find that our focus on each other has reverted back to a focus on ourselves.

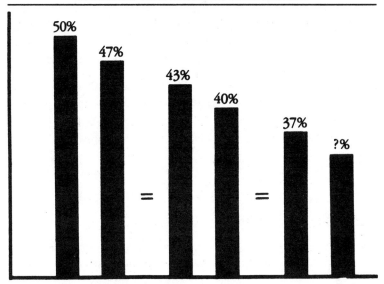

Self-centeredness and loneliness are the inevitable results of 50-50 marriage propositions.

The Gift of Marriage.

Marriage is a covenant with God to totally love one another.

Western Civilization is built on the concept that God created Man and Woman. In our earliest written Scriptures we read that God said that Man was not meant to be alone. Current thought translates these lines to say that Man was not meant to be *lonely*. Yet loneliness is one of the curses of our modern society, both with singles as well as with so many married couples.

Our marriage can be a real gift to each other. There is no love relationship as intimate and less lonely as a positive, dynamic marital relationship. Each of us is unique as a person. Each marriage is also unique. We have the opportunity, by making *decisions to love* one another, to make our marriage one of closeness and togetherness.

55

If we believe that our marriage is a lifelong commitment then marriage cannot be an open door arrangement. I cannot walk away from our marriage if I find I don't feel loving.

We need not conform to the media/marriage style of the current society, going our separate ways when we disagree, or entering into marriage with the idea that if it doesn't work, we can *"split"* with no fault to each other.

Love is not a feeling. Love is a decision!

Pen and Paper Exercise

Accepting our marriage as a lifelong commitment allows us the opportunity for the most intimate level of communication and interdependence. We will be cheating each other unless we actively seek this intimacy.

All other relationships; parents, friends, associates—none of them can be as intimate as we can be as husband and wife.

Marriage is a lifelong commitment, a lifelong career that requires constant work and effort from both of us.

Our marriage will be a covenant by and with God to actively love one another and to care for each other.

Questions - Chapter Five -
Marriage as a Lifelong Commitment

1. How do I feel about committing myself to love you 100% for the rest of my life, realizing that there will be times I may not get anything in return?

2. Do I see our marriage as a commitment?

3. Do I see our marriage as a lifelong commitment?

4. Do I see our marriage as a covenant by and with God?

5. My greatest interest and concern other than our relationship is.......... How do I think this might affect our marriage?

CHAPTER SIX

THE
ETHICS
OF
MARRIAGE

Creating a Meaningful
Set of Standards
for Our Marriage

This chapter spells out more clearly some of the positive consequences of living our marriage as a lifelong commitment. It is meant to be a discussion of setting standards for our marriage that are in tune with historical and meaningful values.

Many couples get married with the idea that they will live their married life day to day and see what comes of it. Others set their sights on having a marriage at least as good as, or a little better than, those whom they observe around them. Others, a few others, not only want the very best that marriage can be, but they are willing to take the actions necessary to attain this type of relationship. Wants, motivations, and desires are nice, but a meaningful, fulfilled marriage doesn't just happen, it takes energy and action.

We can start taking major steps toward this kind of marriage by taking the time now, during our engagement, to set the standards we want for our marriage.

In the previous chapter we discussed marriage as a lifelong commitment. We centered on the idea that Man was not meant to be *"alone."* We discussed *"loneliness"* and emptiness as hidden results of today's "modern" standards.

In this chapter we are going to discuss the ethics of marriage. We are going to discuss marriage ethics as the *positive and creative standards* in our lives, our relationship to one another, and our relationships to others around us. The ethics of marriage is the process of applying agreed-upon, pre-set standards for our everyday married life.

Marriage Ethics.

Ethics involve recognizing, understanding and living out our responsibilities to others as well as recognizing and respecting the rights of others. These ethics are not determined by whether or not we are infringing on someone's rights, or space.

We are going to look at marriage ethics from a point of view that questions whether what we do, or are contemplating doing, advances the life of another person, and not whether it infringes upon them. We are going to look at these ethics to see if what we do, or are contemplating doing, will advance the life of our mate.

Do you think that marriage ethics and standards will:

> *make your life more complete?*
>
> *make you more of a person?*
>
> *make you a better person?*
>
> *it add something to your life?*

We live in a world that teaches amorality. That's a nice phrase for *no morality*.

> *"Do your own thing as long as it doesn't hurt others or restrain others from doing their own thing."*
>
> *"There is no right or wrong, good or evil."*
>
> *"What is right for me may not be right for you."*
>
> *"Personal freedom is more important than anything else."*
>
> *"Don't judge others, it's none of our business as long as they don't restrain us from our own personal freedom."*

Yet, in truth, everything we do does have an effect on those around us, if only by giving others examples of how to live, or not to live.

And, if in fact, our society really believed that we have no effect on others, why is the same world willing to excuse wrong-doers because of the effect that mothers, fathers, family, schools, or society itself has possibly had on them?

Creating and understanding positive standards for our marriage allows us to live an ethical marriage, with all the benefits that it can bring.

In discussing ethics or morality we are not referring to sex and sexual "dos" and "don'ts." The media world has labeled these words with a narrow meaning that creates an automatic defense mechanism in each of us. We tend to shy away from anything connected with these words and phrases.

Marriage ethics and morality, as we approach them here, refer to the standards of our relationships to others, our obligations and responsibilities to others, and how our actions regarding these standards really do affect each other as well as other people.

These standards are not determined by whether we are infringing on someone's rights, but whether it *advances* their life. Reaching for these types of standards can give us the *potential* for becoming a fully-alive human being; of being free, and of making conscious decisions, not merely following our instincts or feelings.

This type of morality involves being able to act on a set of standards that is well thought out rather than just following what's popular, and what is often a fast changing lists of do's and don'ts, or the current "in" fashion or life-style. Predetermined standards allow us to develop a life-style that is centered on relationship rather than one that focuses on circumstances or personal gain.

Shared Relationship vs Individual Pursuits.

This entire workbook is centered on the creation of a foundation for a meaningful marriage relationship between two people. It is based on the fullest sense of relationship, the total interaction between man and wife. It is not focused on various individual pursuits. Many of the things our society values focus on individual character traits. They judge us, straight forwardly or subtly, on various parts of our human make-up. We need only to watch any evening of TV sit-coms and the advertisements to understand the media's obsession with various "positive" or "negative" character traits. The way they present it, a single character trait can mark a person for ultimate success or failure.

Media-Based Character Traits

Physical appearance (thin is really in).

Youthfulness (at any age).

Money (unlimited).

Possessions (right cars, clothes, wines).

Life-style (one big travel folder vacation).

Chasing a Trait.

There is a classic film called "10" which is about a successful man who gives up a close personal relationship with a woman with whom he has just about everything in common. He runs off to chase a beautiful girl—a "10," (on a scale from 1 to 10) who he knows practically nothing about— *except* that she is fantastic looking. When he finally does get this beautiful creature, what do you think he has? She is a beautiful alright, but she's also an empty-headed nothing! He chose to pursue a character *trait* instead of a *relationship*.

Although "10" was a movie, and fiction, we all know people who have overlooked the inward beauty of a real relationship to pursue an empty but attractive character trait.

Setting standards for our marriage means consciously focusing on our *relationship* and not just an personal a character *trait*. The truth is, our physical appearance will change as the years go by, and all of the "things" we own will eventually wear out. But if we focus on each other, we will still have a *relationship* that grows more loving over time.

Setting and Applying Positive Standards.

Love is a Decision!

(That phrase again!)

Making love a *decision* instead of a *feeling* is the primary standard we can set for our marriage. It means acting loving even when we don't feel like being loving. It means allowing ourselves to be loved even when we don't feel lovable. It means being conscious about our behavior toward our spouse at all times.

Another high standard is for us to set is to try to be fully present and responsive to each other's needs and to act in a responsible manner toward one another. We must strive to be responsive to each other's needs, desires and goals.

> *"I think that a major change in our relationship occurred when I learned to shut off the six o'clock evening news and really share my day with Sheila. I trained myself to listen to her words and to try to feel her ups and her downs, instead of simple, brushing her off, or interrupting to tell her what my day was like. I have learned to listen to her without planning my response."*

If we set a high standard for trying to be responsible to each other through our openness, honesty and trust and listening, we reach for this standard each time we are sensitive, complimentary, attentive, and patient with each other.

> *"Diet time seems to be most of the time for both of us. But, when David really gets on a good track, I try to reach out and support him fully. I compliment every physical improvement, every new piece of clothing and every positive action he takes. On the other hand, I try to be sensitive enough in helping that he doesn't think I'm pushing him."*

Setting high standards for our marriage also means seeking the best for you and not settling for the minimum. It means looking to the **best of marriages** as examples and not settling for what we see as average marriages. It means not acting complacent when our marriage looks better than those of our friends.

Applying the high standards we have set means that I constantly bring more life to you, by helping you to become a fuller and more alive person by the way I choose to love you. Each time I am about to make a *decision to love* you I need to ask myself what my actions will produce.

Will my actions bring more life to you?

Will they draw forth the best in you?

Will they draw forth the best in me?

Will they enhance my relationship with you?

Will they enhance my relationship with God?

Will they enhance my relationship with others?

Setting high ethical marriage standards is the best way for us to be fully loving toward one another. We must actively work and strive to apply these standards we have set, in order to bring forth the deepest fulfillment of our marriage commitment to one another.

Obstacles to Setting High Marriage Standards.

There are a number of obstacles that may hold us back from setting high standards for our marriage. I create an obstacle:

1. When I refuse to accept responsibility for the effect that my actions may have on others. Or, when I choose to go along with the popular social notion, *"It's OK as long as it doesn't hurt anybody."* This is indifference and is the opposite of being loving.

2. When I hold onto a sense of guilt. Guilt that I harbor inwardly takes the focus off our couple relationship and centers it on myself. This is selfish and can be destructive. Guilt that I face openly and share with my mate may bring about a responsible change.*

3. When I indulge in self-deception and pretension. Or, when I make myself appear to go through the motions of setting standards with you but have not intention of following through on them.

4. When I compare us to other engaged couples we know that may not be doing as well and therefore excuse myself from trying to set standards with you.

5. When I approach our marriage as an obligation than an opportunity to concentrate on our relationship.

---

* The guilt referred to does not imply confession for past deeds that can hurt our present relationship. An important distinction must be made between sharing guilt to enhance our relationship and simply confessing past deeds in order to salve my conscience and pass the guilt on to my spouse to deal with.

6. When I don't think for myself with regard to our relationship. Or, when I let you make all the decisions.

7. When I am content with letting each one of us *"do our own thing."*

8. When I am full of false pride, thinking, *"I don't want anyone telling me what to do!"*

9. When I am full of self-centeredness.

10. When I am just plain selfish.

We have a responsibility, not only to each other, but to God, and to our families and our community to set and attempt to maintain the highest ethical standards in our marriage.

Aids to Creating Marriage Standards.

We need many discussions where we . . .

- Express our inner feelings—don't suppress them.
- Share our thoughts, ideas, opinions and feelings honestly and lovingly with each other.
- Accept each other where and as we are, understanding that personal change and growth will come from within and not from outside pressures.
- Face our disagreements openly and lovingly, remembering the guidelines for arguing.
- Forgive each other and feel free to ask for forgiveness.
- Give each other praise and compliments, bringing out life from each other.
- Decide to give love as a gift, with no strings and no expectations of return, making our love a 100-100% proposition.
- Allow each other freedom and sensitivity by not being oppressive.
- Keep our ideals and try to create an atmosphere of love, life and freedom.
- Never give up on our lifelong commitment!

The question of marriage standards and marriage ethics is not an easy one, nor is it something we can discuss once and put up on a shelf. The discussion of our standards should be an ongoing part of our marriage. There will often be grey areas and confusion. Maintaining high and ethical marriage standards will require discussion, searching, asking others, and above all, honesty.

The Ethics of Marriage

Our Definitions

To act ethical:
- to bring more life to.
- to add to one's total being.
- to be honest with.

Examples:

Generous - *going beyond the minimum.*

Supportive - *bringing out the best in you.*

Sensitive - *being aware of your needs and feelings.*

Selfless - *caring about* **us** *instead of just me.*

To act unethical:
- to act selfish and/or indifferent.
- to be unwilling to be responsible for the effects that my personal actions might have on others.

Examples:

Indifferent - *"It's OK if it doesn't hurt anybody.*

Close-minded - *I've already decided and am just going through the motions."*

Comparing - *"At least I'm not like them."*

Self-centered - *"I can do my own thing. I'm not dependent on, or responsible to you, God or others."*

Pen & Paper Exercise

Questions - Chapter Six - *The Ethics of Marriage*

1. Do I reflect a responsible relationship toward you?

2. Do you reflect a responsible relationship toward me?

3. Describe an occasion when you have added something meaningful to my life.

4. Describe an occasion when I believe I have added something meaningful to your life.

5. What questions about marriage standards and marriage ethics do I think we still need to talk about together?

   - making a decision to love you when I don't feel loving?

   - being completely honest with each other?

   - trusting myself to be open and honest with you?
   - trusting you to be open and honest with me?

   - my listening to you?
   - your listening to me?

   - my patience with you?
   - your patience with me?

   - my awareness of your non-verbal communication?
   - your awareness of my non-verbal communication?

   - my sexual communication to you?
   - your sexual communication to me?

   - my jealousy of you? Explain further.
   - your jealousy of me? Explain further.

   - my attitudes and/or relationship with God?
   - your attitudes and/or relationship with God?
   - our attitudes and/or relationship with God?

   - my attitudes about forgiveness or holding a grudge?
   - your attitudes about forgiveness or holding a grudge?

CHAPTER SEVEN

MAKING DECISIONS TOGETHER IN OUR MARRIAGE

This chapter is a continuation of the last two chapters, *Marriage as a Lifelong Commitment"* and *"The Ethics of Marriage."* *"Marriage as a Lifelong Commitment"* is basically a theoretical discussion. *"The Ethics of Marriage"* is a more practical chapter dealing with standard setting and ethics. *"Making Decisions in Our Marriage"* gets down to specifics.

The purpose of this chapter is to help us recognize that we have practical and specific decisions to make about our marriage and the standards we set for ourselves.

To live our marriage the fullest requires us to constantly make *decisions to love* one another openly and honestly.

Once basic standards are agreed upon we can move ahead with responsible planning in making other decisions necessary for the day to day living of our marriage. These standards will allow us the potential of becoming more fully human. We will become more able to make conscious and ethical decisions, and not decisions based only on our feelings and instincts.

Making Shared Decisions.

Setting marriage standards allows us to build a marriage based on shared responsibilities. It allows me to make choices in agreement with you, with others, God, and my community. It means we make shared decisions, not me making decisions alone. So, before discussing the four areas of standard setting it is important that we look at the steps necessary for making shared decisions.

Making shared decisions requires that we first have a *willingness* to make decisions together. We have to be committed to struggle together as a couple in setting standards and making decisions.

Once a willingness to make shared decisions is agreed upon, it becomes our first basic standard. We can then go on and learn to make decisions based on guidelines of:

1. **Talking together,** *including the discussion of each other's thoughts, ideas, feelings and opinions.* (Also remembering all the rules for listening.)

2. **Searching together** *by gathering the facts about the decision we're attempting to make.* (Use Scriptures, books, libraries, prime sources.)

3. **Asking around together** *to other qualified people in order to find out what guidelines our heritage and teachings give to us; talking with responsible people such as parents, clergy, counselors, and friends.* (Even with people with whom we don't always agree.)

By following these three steps openly and honestly we can come to mutual agreements. We can learn to make shared decisions and be committed to them.

Once we learn to make shared decisions we will discover the peace, not just relief, that come from making a decision, and the willingness to be committed to it.

> *"This workbook is perfect example of a shared decision. We talked about it for years. It became a wistful dream, never quite in reach. But once we took some action, discussed it seriously together, searched out what was available in print, and talked to a number of professionals and clergy, we decided to go ahead and commit ourselves to the project. All the wistfulness disappeared as we jumped into our new commitment."*

Change and Re-evaluation.

We must also be aware that circumstances may change and a decision we made together might have to be re-evaluated and perhaps changed.

> *"Many years ago we had two little children, a nice job, and lived in a pleasant part of the country. We thought it might be time to buy our first house. We talked about it months on end. We searched the area for the right house. We talked to people in the area and real estate people. We finally made a shared decision to go ahead. That same night the phone rang with an offer for a better position in another town. As our circumstances had abruptly changed, we had to re-evaluate and our decision changed accordingly."*

Shared Decisions Require:

1.   *Talking* together.

2.   *Searching* together for the facts.

3.   *Asking* other qualified and responsible people.

All this leading to:

Shared Decisions . . .
 with the understanding of mutual support after the
 decision and the ability to review and change the decision if necessary.

Four Basic Areas
for Marriage Standards.

Marriage standards cover four different areas:

1.   *Our relationship to each other.*

2.   *Our relationship to others.*

3.   *Our relationship to God.*

4.   *Our everyday life situations.*

Our Relationship to Each Other.

The essence of good a relationship is the ability for us to be able and willing to reveal to each other that we are lovable. Being told that we are loved, being complimented and praised for our talents and actions adds, not only to our personal self-image, but to the closeness of our relationship.

Will we strive to constantly recognize that we each have greater or lesser needs and talents?

Will we remember that these different needs and talents may cause jealousy, competition, or a need to suppress or deny these needs and talents?

Will we strive to remain open and honest in discussing our needs with each other?

Will we strive to maintain a level of verbal love, compliments and praise for each other to help build each other's self-image, even when times might seem "rough?"

Couples often trap themselves or their partner into a role.

Will we strive, through shared decisions to allow each other the freedom to grow as an individual?

Will I be open to use my own talents where necessary to help you grow?

Will we strive, through shared decisions to grow and change as a couple?

73

Compromise is very often a necessity for reaching mutual agreement for a shared decision.

Will we be willing to compromise, at times, when necessary, in order to make a shared decision?

Times, circumstances and needs change. Sometimes a shared decision has to be reviewed and adjusted.

If necessary will we be able to change a shared decision?

Will we be able to be open enough to admit possible wrong decisions or changes of circumstances?

Our decisions must be shared decisions and both of us must be willing to promote them fully.

Once we agree on a shared decision, will we strive to support each other even if we're not 100% in agreement?

Our Relationship to Others.

Our Parents.

Eventually we have to become independent from our parents. This does not mean that we have to reject them or the background from which we came. Our independence refers to our willingness to accept adult responsibility in developing our own unique relationship as a couple.

As we leave our parents it is important to maintain affection and care for them. However, our marriage comes first.

Am I willing to place our marriage relationship in front of our family relationships?

Am I willing to maintain or strive for a sense of warmth, love, and caring with my family even though I am married?

Am I willing to strive for a sense of warmth, love and caring with your family?

Our Children.

Now, before our marriage, is the time for full and open discussions regarding our attitudes about children.

Do I consider them possessions?

Do I think you consider them possessions?

Do I consider them a gift from God?

Do I think you consider them a gift from God?

Planning a family must be a shared decision made with full understanding, and we must be aware of the importance of openness to change if circumstances change. Babies have their way of thwarting the best laid plans.

Responsible planning of a family includes examining our attitudes about family size and making decisions according to the guidelines established in the last chapter; *talking together, searching together* for the facts, *asking* responsible people and then making *shared decisions.*

75

Birth control.

> *Do we believe that it is both our responsibility as husband and wife to take the necessary steps to educate ourselves in all various methods available and to mutually agree on what method we will use, if any?*

> *Do we believe that our decision should be ethical in that it shows both concern and responsibility toward each other?*

> *Will we be flexible and realize changed conditions may necessitate changed attitudes and changed decisions?*

If conception is impossible or too dangerous, tenderness and acceptance are important.

> *Will we strive to be open to discussing alternatives, such as adoption or other means?*

> *Could I consider raising a child as my own if it was not my flesh and blood?*

Child rearing.

> *Do we believe that the best thing parents can do for their children is to show their love for one another?*

Our Friends.

The life-styles of single friends may make it necessary for us to slacken some old friendships and develop new mutual friends who will support our commitment to marriage. Often times we find we have friends who are jealous of our marriage, who would pry, or who would even try and draw us apart. Our marriage will cause changes in our lives and the lives of our single friends. We should be aware that we will also have a need for married friends.

Am I willing to back away from friends if they interfere with our marriage?

Do I think you will be willing to back away from friends if they interfere with our marriage?

Are we willing to take the time to search out and develop new married friends?

Our Relationship with God.

We should plan to spend a good deal of time exploring our attitudes about God before we marry. Each of us, no matter what our faith, or the extent of our religious practice or beliefs, contemplates our understanding of God. This is part of the human condition. Whatever our struggle, whatever our faith, even if none, we have to be trusting and discuss our struggles, faith, or lack of faith with each other on an on-going basis. One thing is certain. Whatever we believe or don't believe today, much will change as the years pass.

Do I fear God as One who will punish?

Do I see God as judgemental—One who keeps score?

Do I see Him as a problem-solving God to turn to when we are in trouble? (and do I expect Him to answer?)

Do I think He is a loving God?

Am I going to leave the faith issue and God for future consideration? Is my decision the best decision for us?

Will we practice our religious beliefs together as a couple or alone as individuals?

Our Everyday Life Situations.

Setting standards for our marriage requires us to search this area of our future life together in order to avoid serious surprises. We have to discuss the importance of our money, our time together and our career(s).

Our Money.

How much are we spending now?

Who will handle the money?

Will the money be ours, yours or mine?

How will we handle charity (tzedakah) as an obligation or from our hearts?

Do I think that money will play an important part of our marriage?

Our Time Together.

How will the time we have together be spent?

Will we have enough time for each other?

What will destroy our time together?

How will we manage time?

Our Career(s).

Whose career will come first?

Are we willing to support each other in our careers?

Should we be a two-career family?

Will our marriage come before our careers?

One of the great sadnesses we have all seen in our busy world is when money, work and/or careers have become more important to a husband or wife than their marriage.

> *"There was a time when I believed that my job was more important than our marriage. I can look back now and see how foolish I was. I realized that I was really running from myself and from being open and honest in sharing my attitudes, expectations and especially fears with my wife. In my own insecurities I closed off myself from her. I played all sorts of games with all sorts of rationalizations and justifications. I've since heard exactly the same rationalizations and justifications dozens of times from others whose marriages are shaky or in the process of breaking up.*

"I was anything but ethical, cutting down and taking life from my wife. I was focusing on myself and my own self-pity and not on her. I had stopped making decisions to love her. I was mistakenly waiting for loving feelings instead of doing loving deeds.

"I was lucky. I got my 'act together' and learned to make decisions to be open, loving, and trusting. I learned to act loving and came to 'feel' loving again."

How many couples do we know who aren't together any more? How many do we know whose careers got in the way of their marriage? Or, where too much money, or too little money came between them? How many couples do we know where too much of what our media said was important became more important than their marriage?

"I know how I feel when this happens to my friends. It has happened often enough in the past few years. I hurt for them. I hurt for their loneliness. I hurt for their lost love that was there all along if only they had decided to risk a little openness with each other before it was too late. If only they had been able to make decisions to love instead of believing that the 'feeling' had just gone away," they might still be together today."

Pen & Paper Exercise.

This exercise should take at least thirty minutes to write. Plan plenty of time for discussion.

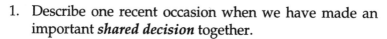

Questions - Chapter Seven -
Decisions in Our Marriage

1. Describe one recent occasion when we have made an important *shared decision* together.

   Do I think this decision was ethical?

   How seriously did we *discuss* the matter before making our decision?

   How did we *search together* for facts and alternatives?

   With whom else did we *talk together* besides each other?

   Did we reach a *shared decision* and both carry it out? Do I think we are both willing to be responsible for the results of our *shared decision?*

   Do I think we are both willing to *review the decision* and change it if circumstances change?

2. What *shared decision* have we made that I am proud of?

   Did we follow the proper steps to make that *shared decision?*

3. What decision have we made that I believed was wrong or that I regretted?

   Did we follow the proper steps to make that decision?

4. Do I think I am willing to compromise when we can't reach a *shared decision?*

5. Do I think you are willing to compromise when we can't reach a *shared decision?*

6. In what area am I jealous of you and how do I think I should change?

7. In what area do I think you are jealous of me and how do I think you should change?

8. What kind of relationship do I hope we will have with my parents?

9. What kind of relationship do I hope we will have with your parents?

10. What kind of relationship do I hope we will have with my friends?

11. What kind of relationship do I hope we will I have with your friends?

12. How close do I think we are in agreeing on when we will have a child?

    Have we really made a *shared decision* on this?

13. Am I satisfied with my concept of God?

    Am I looking for something different in my relationship with God?

14. How do I think we can support each others faith and religious beliefs?

15. How will we share our leisure time as a couple?

16. What decisions about my career do we have to make as a result of our marriage?

17. What decisions about your career do we have to make as a result of our marriage?

CHAPTER EIGHT

ONENESS

THE
ULTIMATE
GOAL
OF
MARRIAGE

Happiness is a feeling.
Oneness involves a relationship.

The purpose of this chapter is to demonstrate that happiness is not the ultimate goal of marriage. *Oneness* is the goal.

Oneness is the loving and close relationship that can develop from a growing and alive marriage as the partners experience life together.

To reach this state of *oneness* in our marriage requires the constant awareness of and active making of daily decisions to love one another. These decisions to love are a part of working at our marriage. They are the manifestation of our constant striving to achieve a state of *oneness*.

We have all observed couples that seem to have their lives together as a cohesive, almost single unit. They seem "to have it together" with their marriage. In some cases, they actually appear to glow. Their love for each other is obvious. It's not just a physical look, but somewhat of an aura that surrounds them. There is no question that they are married to each other. There is no question that they are in love. If we see one of them without the other, we have the feeling that something is missing. They just don't look right when they are not together. They have achieved a level of *oneness* in their relationship.

We are referring to couples who have been married for some time, not the engaged or recently wed. These special, tight knit couples have a more "long term" look that shows the positive years spent together.

One of the interesting things about many of these "long term" couples is that they may not have life-styles or live lives that some consider *"living a happy life."* Even though they don't appear to have a high standard of living and may have suffered great tragedy in their lifetime, they appear so "together." Happiness is not the reason their togetherness. Their special *oneness* is the reason.

Happiness can be, and usually is, a transitory feeling. Happiness can come and go, be subject to moods swings, outside influences, and factors beyond our control. Happiness today is more often tied to our possessions and money, rather than our relationships. It tends to be material and place oriented and not people oriented. On the other hand, *oneness* is relationship oriented — *other*-person oriented.

Marriage gives us the opportunity to create a special kind of *oneness*. It's a *oneness* is not based on feelings. It is the result of our conscious and active *decisions to love* each other. It upholds our marriage standards by keeping the focus on our marriage and each other.

Feelings of happiness often accompany *oneness*. But, more often, *oneness* is described by those special couples as a feeling of inner peace. Inner peace is not a phrase often heard in today's anxiety-ridden and feeling-conscious world. As a married couple, we have the *potential* of a state of being that is yearned for, yet almost unattainable within the popular cultural values of our society.

Our media trains us to believe that we can buy things to make us feel happy. Our personal experiences show how fleeting this happiness can be. When we were children we yearned for special toys because we were told by the media that they would make us feel happy. If we got the toys, we felt happy, for a while, but those feeling passed quickly and life continued on.

"Every time I feel down I find myself out shopping. In the back of my mind I am saying that buying something will bring forth the happy feelings I am looking for. I might buy a new suit and feel good about it. But once bought, the suit goes in my closet until I need it while everything else in my life goes on.

"I have a collection of all sorts of things to make me feel happy. I have my stereo, my car, my computer, my camera and my other special things. Buying each of them was a special event. I felt happy buying. I had the media's vision of walking off into the sunset feeling happy—forever after.

"My stereo is out of date now with CDs and the new digital recording systems. My car is a year old with a few dings in it and the newer models are out. My computer needs more memory to do the work I think I would like to do with it because my computer programs are no longer the state of the art. My camera doesn't have all the latest gadgets. My other special things sit here and there, not bringing to me the magic feeling of happiness implied with their purchase."

In marriage we find that the same disappointments or let-downs come if we think material things will bring us lasting happiness. We might have feelings of happiness in the pride we have for the possessions we own. These possessions might be such things as our house, our car(s), our motor home, our clothes, our collections or our boat.

But this kind of happiness can disappear due to a variety of external circumstances. I might lose my job. We might have a financial crisis. One of us might get sick. There may be a death in the family. I might fail in my career. Possessions can go, and with them many of our feelings of happiness. A marriage requiring happiness, or with happiness as its ultimate goal, won't be able to withstand adverse circumstances.

However, a marriage built on striving to achieve *oneness* can weather most storms and become even closer in the process. We cannot control the feelings of happiness, but we can constantly make decisions to bring about *oneness*. In the cases where we focus on *oneness*, happiness often comes to us as a fringe benefit.

Oneness comes from love and commitment to each other and to God. It is a goal we can strive for as a married couple.

Oneness is Not . . .

Oneness, by our definition, is not sameness or uniformity. I don't have to look like you, dress like you or act like you.

Oneness, by our definition, is not external "togetherness." We have all experienced couples who look so loving in public for the sake of image, but who are distant from each other in private.

Oneness, by our definition, does not require the sacrifice of our individuality. As a couple we are still made up of two separate and unique individuals. However, *oneness* may require the sacrifice or adjustment of our individual goals in order to be able to focus on and better care for the needs of one another.

Oneness, by our definition, does not imply submission or false harmony. As a couple we should strive for both equality and openness. *Oneness* comes through freedom. *Oneness* will not be achieved if I make you do things my way, or expect you to think and act as I do.

Confidence Builds *Oneness.*

Confidence in each others' love allows us to search and become more ourselves. Confidence comes as the result of striving together to set and live with a high standard of ethics in marriage. The confidence we gain from each other leads us to our *oneness.*

Oneness requires a constant building process which can never be taken for granted or achieved alone. We are human and incapable of perfect love. *Oneness* requires a constant state of striving for more.

Results of *Oneness.*

While *oneness* needs freedom to begin, it also generates greater freedom to be ourselves. It removes anxieties and helps us to be more open and to share more honestly. It is a cushion against the jealousy and suspicion that may develop from time to time in our marriage. *Oneness* helps us to be ourselves and not just another couple measured by the standards of the modern world. *Oneness* gives us the confidence to be free.

Society claims that the *oneness* we describe would be restrictive to the individual. We claim that the *oneness* that we describe frees the individual from the anxieties of society. In a state of *oneness* I am more free and more confident to be an individual and not restricted or restrained by the cultural, and "in fashion" demands of society. I have the confidence to be more in control of myself.

Knowing I am loved by you can give me this unique freedom, confidence and inner peace.

Pen and Paper Exercise.
Questions - Chapter Eight
Oneness, The Ultimate Goal

1. When have I felt close to you, sharing my concerns as well as my joys?

2. When have I felt the greatest need to be close to you?

3. How have I withheld myself from you because of my lack of confidence in our love? *Explain, be specific.*

4 . What is my concept of *oneness* in marriage?

5 . Do I believe that *oneness*, not happiness, is the real goal of marriage?

6 . What do I think we might do differently to strive for *oneness* in our relationship?

CHAPTER NINE
A
BETROTHAL
PLEDGE
TO
OUR
FUTURE

The purpose of this chapter is to help us, as an engaged couple, become aware of the preparation needed before reciting our marriage vows. This period of our engagement can be a time to deepen our communication levels and our relationship before God and our faith community. It can be a time to lay solid foundations of communication on which our marriage can be built.

This chapter will allow us the opportunity to write a betrothal pledge to each other, one we can keep and use as a specific guide for the rest of our engagement.

The Six Major Points.

There have been six major points in the preceding chapters.

1. Marriage is a lifelong career, not a swinging door to walk away from if the "feelings" appear to be missing.

2 . How we live our lives and our marriage does have an effect on other people, if only to give them examples on how to live their lives.

3. We can't change each other. We can only set the loving atmosphere and give the encouragement necessary for each of us to grow and change.

4. Perceived problems are usually not the real problem. Thinking that differences will <u>not</u> be a problem is the real problem. We have to start discussing those differences now, before marriage.

5. The ultimate goal of marriage is oneness, not happiness. Oneness involves relationship. Happiness involves feelings.

   and

6. *Love is a decision*—a behavior, not a feeling!

This workbook is an invitation for us to look beyond our engagement and to understand that there is so much more possible in our relationship. Our engagement can be a time of preparation for our lives ahead and not only the period of time necessary to plan a fancy affair.

Making a Betrothal Pledge to Each Other.

When we announced our engagement we went beyond just making the statement of fact, "We are engaged," which put our wedding plans into motion. By making that announcement we pledged to love each other and we pledged to prepare ourselves to be a married couple. We made that announcement to more than just ourselves. Whether we were aware of it or not, we made our announcement to our family, our friends, to God and to our community.

On our wedding day, during the ceremony, we will be asked to commit ourselves to each other until death. We should ask ourselves some important questions now:

Who is really asking this question?

   Is it the clergy?

   Is it our parents?

   Is it our friends?

   Is it God?

   Is it the community?

What does it mean to be married in our faith?

Are we part of it? Do we belong to it?

In this chapter we are going to ask you to write a betrothal pledge to each other. It will be a letter that sums up your hopes and expectations from now until the moment you take your wedding vows.

How do we choose to write this betrothal pledge?

Our betrothal pledge can be either a statement of facts which might lead to a mere legal contract, or it can be a sincere, loving pledge that openly announces that we are preparing for a meaningful married life.

Our betrothal pledge can be a symbol that we are a part of our heritage, the generations past and the generations to come. As a newly married couple, we become the hope for the future.

Preparation for writing our betrothal pledge.

I will write my betrothal pledge in order to build a deeper relationship with you. I will write this pledge in order to build a better foundation of communication and love from which our marriage can grow.

I will write this pledge in order to better change my focus from *me and you,* to *we and us* and on to our common goals. Writing this pledge will allow me an opportunity to put some of our marriage standards and shared decision making concepts into effect that we discussed in earlier chapters.

Note: *If you are not ready to make a commitment to write this betrothal pledge, continue on with this chapter. However, instead of writing the pledge, share honestly, and in writing, just where you think you are in your relationship. A couple may love each other very deeply and agree they are not ready for marriage or that they need more time to work on their relationship. If you now believe this might be your situation, use the writing time and discussion time afterwards to share with your fiance(e) why you believe you couldn't write a betrothal pledge now.*

Pen and Paper Exercise

Questions - Chapter Nine -
Our Betrothal Pledge.

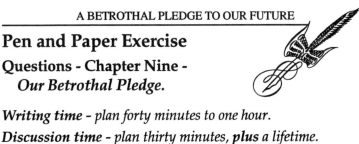

Writing time - plan forty minutes to one hour.
*Discussion time - plan thirty minutes, **plus** a lifetime.*

Love is a decision!

Make a decision to write with love, honesty, trust and understanding. Be sure to write this exercise as you might write a love letter to each other.

There are no specific questions this time. You are to write whatever you want, directly from your heart.

One example of how you might start your betrothal pledge might be.....

> *My, dearest . . . .*
> *Because I love you, I plan to work on communicating openly with you by . . . . .*
> *then . . . .*

1. List the various categories you wish to write about based on your discussions derived from following the workbook. One word or phrase will usually do, to keep as a reminder while you write the full letter.

2. Decide which areas you believe are ***most*** important.

3. Starting with the most important area, write as completely as possible about the subject and describe how you hope to work on it during the time left before your wedding day.

4. If you still have time, go on to the second area of importance, repeat the process.

5. If you find that you only have time for one topic, that's OK. Most people rarely finish the first area on which they begin to write. Use any subjects from the entire workbook. Concentrate on areas where you had the longest, and perhaps most difficult discussions

Please note:

If you believe you are unable to make a commitment to work on a particular area which you think might be a problem in your marriage, write a different kind of letter to your fiance(e).

Write an open and honest letter defining the area in which you *cannot* delve further. Be open and honest. Share where you are now, and perhaps, why you think that you cannot share about that area at this time.

Some couples love each other very deeply and agree that there are areas that they cannot yet share.

You may love each other very deeply and come to understand that you are not yet ready for marriage and that you need more time to work on your relationship. If you believe you fall into this category, it is most important to take this time to explain why you believe that you are not ready to write a betrothal pledge. If you write your letter honestly, you may find you really **are** ready. Let your love for your fiance(e) allow you to be honest.

Make a decision to love!

CHAPTER TEN

OUR
WEDDING

A
SYMBOL
OF OUR
HERITAGE

One purpose of this chapter is to make us aware that with the reciting of our wedding vows we are to become a symbol of our heritage. Generations upon generations have come before us, each adding to the values and goodness that make up the *positive potential* that is within each of us. How we live, how we act together as a married couple will add to that long chain—our heritage—as we pass on part of ourselves to the generations to come. How we live and how we act together will also have an effect on other people around us, and that, in turn, will have an effect on the generations to follow them. Upon the recitation of our wedding vows we begin living our lifelong commitment to our marriage.

A second purpose of this chapter is to encourage us to recognize the joy of our love and to share it with others, not keep it just to ourselves. We have a responsibility to be generous with our love.

Reciting Our Wedding Vows.

Our wedding vows solemnize our betrothal pledge to each other and to God. Our wedding vows are a symbol of God's presence in our marriage. Wherever we recite our vows, in a synagogue, a church, our home, a park, a social hall, or even an office, we become a symbol of God's presence to each other and to the world. Our society, especially what is known as Western society is "Scripture" based. The earliest of scriptures, *Genesis*, written or given sometime in our ancient beginnings as a civilization, set down the primary nature of marriage and its relationship of God to Mankind. Whether or not we believe in our past or in the teachings of our heritage, the moral structure of the society in which we live has its deepest foundations based on this concept.

Marriage is a living and ongoing symbol, not just a moment of our wedding. But it will be so, only as long as we live our vows and seek to grow in mutual love and respect.

Western civilization views our marriage as a covenant between ourselves and our relationship with God. This covenant allows us to share our lives and ideals. It allows us to grow through each other's love and to become a symbol of fidelity and goodness to the world around us. How we live our marriage is observed by others and can have a **positive** effect on their lives. We will effect other people by our love and by our actions as a married couple. We are not alone in this world.

Most couples spend so much time on the physical symbols of their wedding that they fail to see, or take the time to understand, the importance of their wedding to the community that surrounds them. They get so wrapped up in wedding gowns and invitations, social halls and table settings that they forget that they are actually forging a link in the chain between the past and the future.

Why do people cry at weddings? Even the strongest man will admit to feeling the pain of holding back tears that are trying to surface. This reaction must come from something a bit more than seeing a white gown and happy couple?

How many memories come to the surface?

How many covered or lost ideals push to the surface?

How much hope for the future is felt?

Those who are witnessing the wedding are contending with strong emotional reactions to it, while the bridal couple seems to be wrapped up in being careful not to trip, making sure Aunt Sarah has a good seat, or seeing that the flowers look just right.

Wedding Magic.

Wouldn't it be exciting if we could be aware of the magic that our wedding and the reciting of our vows was having *inside* of those who are witnessing our marriage? During our ceremony we should try to remember to brush aside our worries about the mechanics of our wedding and focus more on each other. We should try to reach out to our guests with our hearts and to experience what is going on *inside* of those who are sharing this day with us. Our wedding will have a powerful effect on them, if we're aware of this. And as we stand together repeating our vows, we will be affecting other lives at that moment.

Our Marriage
is the Hope
for the Future of
Mankind

Reaching Out to Others.

We sometimes get caught up in ourselves as individuals, and the same thing can happen to us as a couple. We can become centered on "us," become selfish and begin to see everything only in terms of how it will effect "us." The inevitable result is disillusionment. We wake up alone or together one day thinking or saying, *"Is that all there is?"*

When we express our love we find it has the opposite effect. The more of our love we give, the more love we find we have to share. Think of the most loving people you know. Who are the most loving people in our families, our circle of friends, in the community around us? They will be the ones that share their love with others. Now ask yourself who are the least loving people you know. They will usually be the most insular, the most dissatisfied and the most lonely.

If we believe that the way we will live our lives is our own business, and that our lives will have no effect on others, then we might as well live our lives alone. If, on the other hand, we believe that we will affect the lives of others, by our actions and by our marriage, then we will have the responsibility to reach out to others. The choice is ours. We will have the choice to turn inward toward ourselves or face outwards toward the world. Facing inward requires no action. Facing outward requires a shared *decision to love.*

Sharing Our Love.

One of the ways we can begin sharing our love is at our wedding. We might consider inviting **all** of our relatives, *especially* the family outcasts. Our wedding can be a great place for healing old family wounds. Weddings have a special healing magic of their own. The potential results are more than worth the risk.

Who in the family should be invited that we would normally avoid?

What old wounds might be patched at our wedding?

We should also give special consideration to the neighbor(s), friend(s), or teacher(s) that have had a special influence on our lives. These people are usually not aware of their influence because we seldom tell them.

What teacher had a special effect on my life?

What neighbor made a difference to me when I was growing up as a child?

What old, past, forgotten friend molded part of me that I believe is important to my adult makeup?

These people are usually forgotten in wedding plans, or never even thought of. Just think of the great pleasure we can give to these special people if they are included at our wedding. Just think how they will feel when they are told why they were invited.

A Gift of Our Betrothal Pledges.

If we are going to help create the liturgy of our marriage, we might reflect on our awareness of each other and of our place in the community by including all or part of what we wrote in our betrothal pledges in the last chapter. We probably wrote some profound statements, the kind of statements of love and commitment that the rest of the world longs to hear today. These statements could be a beautiful gift, not only to each other, but also to our wedding guests.

We Become a Symbol.

On our wedding day we become a symbol of our heritage. Our married lives continue that symbol and keep it alive by caring for one another. We keep this symbol alive for the world to see by constantly making *decisions to love* each other. Each *decision to love* is reciting our vow— "*I will*" — that we will say to each other on our wedding day.

Our wedding vows will sanctify the standards we set for our marriage. Consciously living our vows and striving to live up to our standards will strengthen our own marriage as well as others that we meet. Our marriage is the hope for the future, for the civilized future of Mankind.

Pen and Paper Exercise.

Questions - Chapter Ten -
Our Wedding

1. What does our being married mean to me today?

2 What does becoming a symbol of God's covenant mean to me at this moment?

3. Do I see our marriage as being important to other married couples?

4. Do I believe that how we will live our marriage will affect other marriages? Does it matter?

5. What can we do at our wedding that will be meaningful to our guests?

6. Whom can we invite that we normally would have forgotten or would have purposely left out?

7. What can we do to experience a bit of what is going on *inside* our guests while we recite our wedding vows?

CHAPTER ELEVEN

SETTING GOALS FOR OUR LIVES TOGETHER

The purpose of this chapter is for us to start setting our goals and objectives goals and objectives for our lives together down on paper, and to start working on specific plans for eventual results.

Our goals and our objectives shape our lives and our marriage. Yet often, engaged couples don't know each other's hopes for the future. It is important in planning our lives together that we understand each other's hopes and dreams. It is important that we start planning before our wedding for our future goals and objectives.

Objectives

In discussing our hopes and plans it is important to separate what we understand as our short term objectives and our long range goals. Long range goals can be general. They can cover a broad area, such as income range, field of work or place in the community.

Short range objectives are different. Time creeps up on them rapidly. Therefore, these objectives must be measurable. We have to be able to take stock of our progress, to keep score, so to speak. We have to be able to pause and judge how well we are doing.

Short term objectives are such things as the timing of our first child, or even how many children we would like. When will we move into our first home, or will it be a condominium? What kind of vacation do we want next year? What kind of car will we buy first. When should I expect a promotion?

Just as important, we have to be aware that our short term objectives are subject to priority changes. Our vacation or special car priority can change rapidly when an unexpected baby announces its arrival. A job promotion that requires a transfer to a new location can change a housing goal. A shortage of money can change the type of car we can afford. Sickness can change vacation plans.

Short term objectives need flexibility. We should even expect changes with reasonable certainty.

Long term goals can be more rigid. A long term goal can be reached by many different paths.

Our Goals Shape Our Lives.

Because our goals shape our lives, it is important that we make our plans together. Using the techniques of shared decisions we have learned, we can better plan our lives, shape our future, and generally be in better control of our lives.

From the beginning of our relationship we've each had plans of some kind. We may not have shared them with each other. We may have simply gone from day to day with what each of us thought was an *"understanding."* But far too often, couples wake up one day and discover that they are each living out a different set of plans and reaching for different goals. By traveling these different paths they will find they have *"grown apart."*

By setting our goals and objectives together *before* marriage, we can better insure our traveling the same path of life together.

In writing the final exercise we are going to separate again. We will answer the questions as individuals, then come back together and share our answers. After discussing them, we are to *combine* our answers, *in writing*, creating an initial set of goals and objectives together. This will be a major starting point toward setting more permanent goals and objectives for our marriage.

The areas we cover will have to be talked about, planned and re-planned throughout our marriage. We may discover that some plans we had discussed in the past might have to be changed in light of what we've learned while following the steps outlined in this workbook. That's great! It means we've grown even more, and that we can be sure we will continue to grow and change. Our need for planning and reviewing our goals and objectives will never cease.

Most of all, never forget -

Love is Not a Feeling!   Love is a Decision!

Pen & Paper Exercise.

Questions - Chapter Eleven - *Setting Goals*

A. What do I consider short term goals (our first married year) regarding:
1. Job(s), career(s) - kind and position?
2. Income - how much - you, me, us?
3. Size and location of home?
4. Our place in the community?
5. Having a child?

B. What do I consider mid-term goals (5 years from now) regarding:
1. Job(s), career(s) - kind and position?
2. Income - how much - you, me, us?
3. Size and location of home?
4. Our place in the community?
5. Number of children?

C. What do I consider as a potential long term goal (20 years from now) regarding:
1. Job(s), career(s) - kind and position?
2. Income - total family income?
3. Our place in the community?
4. Our marriage and our family life?
5. Our relationship to each other?

Duplicate Set of Questions

Cut these questions out and place in one of your journals.

One person can use the questions on these pages, while the other uses the questions at the end of each chapter.

Questions - Chapter One - *The Search for Myself.*

1. What are some of the specific good qualities I would like others to see in me? What are some of the nice things about me that I would like other people to notice?

2. What qualities do others see in me? *(Give a few examples of compliments you tend to receive from others.)*

3. How do I see myself? *(What is my self-image?)*

   What do I like about myself? *(Be specific.)*

   What do I dislike about myself? *(Explain in detail)*

4. What specific personal characteristics do I see in myself that I think make it more difficult for you (my fiancee) to love me?

Remember, this writing is private and for your eyes only.

Chapter Two

First write a fast outline or short phrases. Then, rewrite each of them as a letter to your fiance(e). Make each a long letter. Be honest and be open. Understand that your fiance(e) knows you far better than you might believe.

Do not write what you think he/she might want to read. Write the truth. Allow yourself to be vulnerable. It's OK. Remember, ***love is a decision.***

When you are both through writing, exchange your letters with each other. Read them quietly. Perhaps you might wish to read them aloud to each other. When you are finished, talk about them. When you believe you have said all there is to say to each other, go on to the next chapter.

Plan about thirty minutes to write your answers to these questions.

Questions - Chapter Two - *Love is a Decision*

1. When do I think I have experienced romance in our relationship?

2. When do I think I have experienced disillusionment in our relationship?

3. When have I made a conscious decision to love you even though I didn't "feel" loving at that time?

4. When have I made a conscious decision to allow you to love me even though I didn't *"feel"* lovable at that time?

5. In what areas of our life do I find that loving you takes a decision? *(Explain fully.)*

105

6. List two ways you and your fiancee are alike and describe each of them.

7 .List two ways you believe you and your fiance(e) differ and describe each of them.

Questions - Chapter Three - *Openness is Also a Decision*

1. What positive things about myself (thoughts, feelings, actions, dreams) do I find difficult to reveal to you?

2. What negative things about myself , (same), do I find difficult to reveal to you?

3. In what areas of our relationship have I been afraid to risk being open with you? (Explain)

4. In what areas of our relationship do I think you have been afraid to risk being open with me? (Explain).

   Draw your answers from the areas listed below for each of the questions above.

   a. Our responsibilities in our marriage.
   b. Our roles in our marriage.
   c. Our sex life.
   d. Our children.
   e. Our religion.
   f. Our in-laws.
   g. Our money.
   h. Our drinking or drug habits.
   i. Our careers - yours and mine.
   j. The way you treat me.
   k. Our friends - yours and mine.
   l. Our health - yours and mine.
   m. Other areas. (Explain).

5. Do I think I listen to you?

6. Do I think you listen to me?

Chapter Four

Write your answers to all the questions. *Write the longest answers to the questions you don't want to answer at all!* Be honest and trusting.

When finished, exchange your answers with your fiancee again and read each others' pages. Plan plenty of time to discuss your answers.

Questions - Chapter Four - *Signposts of a Closed Relationship*

1. What are the things I talk to others about more easily than I do with you?

   Do I trust someone else more than you? *(at least in some areas).* *Explain.*

2. Do I think you confide in someone else more than me? Whom do I think it is and why do I think you do?

3. What difficulties do I have with myself that hold me back from writing and sharing myself honestly with you now?

   What difficulties do I have with you that hold me back from writing and sharing myself honestly with you now?

4. Do I have any doubts about marrying you? What are they?

5. Do I think you have any doubts about marrying me? What might they be?

6. Are our wedding plans primarily shared between us, divided up, or all one-sided?

   Do I think it ought to be shared differently?

7. What are the things that make me angry with you? Explain each item more fully.

8. Am I jealous of you? In what ways?

9. In what areas must I have my own way? Why?

10. What areas am I still afraid to discuss with you? Why?

    What areas do I think you are still afraid to discuss with me? Why?

Questions - Chapter Five - *Marriage as a Lifelong Commitment*

1. How do I feel about committing myself to love you 100% for the rest of my life, realizing that there will be times I may not get anything in return?

2. Do I see our marriage as a commitment?

3. Do I see our marriage as a lifelong commitment?

4. Do I see our marriage as a covenant by and with God?

5. My greatest interest and concern other than our relationship is..........

   How do I think this might affect our marriage?

Questions - Chapter Six - *The Ethics of Marriage*

1. Do I reflect a responsible relationship toward you?

2. Do you reflect a responsible relationship toward me?

3. Describe an occasion when you have added something meaningful to my life.

4. Describe an occasion when I believe I have added something meaningful to your life.

5. What questions about marriage standards and marriage ethics do I think we still need to talk about together?

   • making a decision to love you when I don't feel   loving?

   • being completely honest with each other?

- trusting myself to be open and honest with you?
- trusting you to be open and honest with me?

- my listening to you?
- your listening to me?

- my patience with you?
- your patience with me?

- my awareness of your non-verbal communication?
- your awareness of my non-verbal communication?

- my sexual communication to you?
- your sexual communication to me?

- my jealousy of you? Explain further.
- your jealousy of me? Explain further.

- my attitudes and/or relationship with God?
- your attitudes and/or relationship with God?
- our attitudes and/or relationship with God?

- my attitudes about forgiveness or holding a grudge?
- your attitudes about forgiveness or holding a grudge?

Questions - Chapter Seven - *Decisions in Our Marriage*
This exercise should take at least thirty minutes to write. Plan plenty of time for discussion.

1. Describe one recent occasion when we have made an important *shared decision* together.

   Do I think this decision was ethical?

   How seriously did we *discuss* the matter before making our decision?

   How did we *search together* for facts and alternatives?

   With whom else did we *talk together* besides each other?

   Did we reach a *shared decision* and both carry it out? Do I think we are both willing to be responsible for the results of our *shared decision?*

   Do I think we are both willing to *review the decision* and change it if circumstances change?

2. What *shared decision* have we made that I am proud of?

   Did we follow the proper steps to make that *shared decision?*

3. What decision have we made that I believed was wrong or that I regretted?

   Did we follow the proper steps to make that decision?

4. Do I think I am willing to compromise when we can't reach a *shared decision?*

5 . Do I think you are willing to compromise when we can't reach a *shared decision?*

6. In what area am I jealous of you and how do I think I should change?

7. In what area do I think you are jealous of me and how do I think you should change?

8 . What kind of relationship do I hope we will have with my parents?

9. What kind of relationship do I hope we will have with your parents?

10. What kind of relationship do I hope we will have with my friends?

11. What kind of relationship do I hope we will I have with your friends?

12. How close do I think we are in agreeing on when we will have a child? Have we really made a *shared decision* on this?

13. Am I satisfied with my concept of God?

    Am I looking for something different in my relationship with God?

14. How do I think we can support each others faith and religious beliefs?

15. How will we share our leisure time as a couple?

16. What decisions about my career do we have to make as a result of our marriage?

17. What decisions about your career do we have to make as a result of our marriage?

Questions - Chapter Eight - *Oneness, The Ultimate Goal*

1. When have I felt close to you, sharing my concerns as well as my joys?

2. When have I felt the greatest need to be close to you?

3. How have I withheld myself from you because of my lack of confidence in our love? *Explain, be specific.*

4 . What is my concept of *oneness* in marriage?

5 . Do I believe that *oneness*, not happiness, is the real goal of marriage?

6 . What do I think we might do differently to strive for *oneness* in our relationship?

Questions - Chapter Nine - *Our Betrothal Pledge.*
Writing time - plan forty minutes to one hour.

*Discussion time - plan thirty minutes, **plus** a lifetime.*

Love is a decision!

Make a decision to write with love, honesty, trust and understanding. Be sure to write this exercise as you might write a love letter to each other.

There are no specific questions this time. You are to write whatever you want, directly from your heart.

One example of how you might start your betrothal pledge might be.....

> *My, dearest* . . . .
>
> *Because I love you, I plan to work on communicating openly with you by* . . . . .
>
> *then* . . . .

1. List the various categories you wish to write about based on your discussions derived from following the workbook. One word or phrase will usually do, to keep as a reminder while you write the full letter.

2 . Decide which areas you believe are *most* important.

3. Starting with the most important area, write as completely as possible about the subject and describe how you hope to work on it during the time left before your wedding day.

4. If you still have time, go on to the second area of importance, repeat the process.

5. If you find that you only have time for one topic, that's OK. Most people rarely finish the first area on which they begin to write. Use any subjects from the entire workbook. Concentrate on areas where you had the longest, and perhaps hardest, discussions

Please note:

If you believe you are unable to make a commitment to work on a particular area which you think might be a problem in your marriage, write a different kind of letter to your fiance(e).

Write an open and honest letter defining the area in which you *cannot* delve further. Be open and honest. Share where you are now, and perhaps, why you think that you cannot share at this time.

Some couples love each other very deeply and agree that there are areas that they can not yet share.

You may love each other very deeply and come to understand that you are not yet ready for marriage and that you need more time to work on your relationship. If you believe you fall into this category, it is most important to take this time to explain why you believe that you are not ready to write a betrothal pledge. If you write your letter honestly, you may find you really **are** ready. Let your love for your fiance(e) allow you to be honest.

Make a decision to love!

Questions - Chapter Ten - *Our Wedding*

1. What does our being married mean to me today?

2 What does becoming a symbol of God's covenant mean to me at this moment?

3. Do I see our marriage as being important to other married couples?

4. Do I believe that how we will live our marriage will affect other marriages? Does it matter?

5. What can we do at our wedding that will be meaningful to our guests?

6. Whom can we invite that we normally would have forgotten or would have purposely left out?

7. What can we do to experience a bit of what is going on *inside* our guests while we recite our wedding vows?

Questions - Chapter Eleven - *Setting Goals*

A. What do I consider short term goals (in our first married year) regarding:

    1. Job(s), career(s) - kind and position?

    2. Income - how much - you, me, us?

    3. Size and location of home?

    4. Our place in the community?

    5. Having a child?

B. What do I consider mid-term goals (5 years from now) regarding:

    1. Job(s), career(s) - kind and position?

    2. Income - how much - you, me, us?

    3. Size and location of home?

    4. Our place in the community?

    5. Number of children?

C. What do I consider as a potential long term goal (20 years from now) regarding:

    1. Job(s), career(s) - kind and position?

    2. Income - total family income?

    3. Our place in the community?

    4. Our marriage and our family life?

    5. Our relationship to each other?

Order Additional Copies of

The Art of Engagement

for

- friends,
- relatives,
- grown children,
- newly engaged couples

Help them build a strong
foundation of communication
for a long lasting marriage.

Send $12.95 to:

The Isaac Nathan Publishing Co., Inc.
22711 Cass Avenue
Woodland Hills, CA 91364

We pay postage and handling!
California Residents add $1.10 for Sales Tax

*Send along a signed gift card and
we will send it directly to them from you.*